BECOMING

— AN —

ENGINEER

The Average Person's Guide to
Getting Good Grades and
Succeeding in Engineering School
(and STEM)

Jake Ryland

For those who think they can't

If you find this book helpful, please share it with your friends and classmates. And please don't forget to leave a review on Amazon. It is one of the most powerful things you can do to help others find this book. Thank you!

TABLE OF CONTENTS

SEVEN - STUDYING PART 1: WHERE AND WHEN

EIGHT - STUDYING PART 2: HOW

NINE - EXAMS

ONE

WHY YOU SHOULD TRUST ME

I am not a smart man.
—Forrest Gump

Why do engineering students struggle so much? Why is the average grade point average (GPA) only 2.9? And why are nearly half of all students failing to graduate?[1] Is the course material just too complex? Are that many students simply not smart enough? *No!* Let me make this perfectly clear. The primary variables that will determine if you do or do not graduate have absolutely nothing to do with your IQ. I know—I scored a seventeen on the ACT (thirty-first percentile), failed the college placement exam, and never made it past algebra in high school. Yet, I graduated

---

[1] American Society for Engineering Education. "Engineering by the Numbers: ASEE Retention and Time-to-Graduation Benchmarks for Undergraduate Engineering Schools, Departments and Programs." Washington, DC: Brian L. Yoder, 2016.

with two engineering degrees and a 3.8 GPA. My success was possible because I addressed the *real* problems that plague all engineering students. I am sick and tired of watching would-be great engineers fall victim to the same obstacles over and over. It's about time someone shed some light on what it *really* takes to be successful. This book is the collection of what I and so many others have had to learn the hard way. It is the much-needed road map for success in engineering and STEM. You *can* get any degree you want, and this book will show you how.

Why This Book Was Written

Reason 1: The World Needs More Engineers. Currently, there are 7.6 billion people on this planet with another 83 million joining every year. If we expect our standard of living to keep increasing while also maintaining the health of the planet, then we are going to need *a lot* more engineers, scientists, and innovators. There are innumerable challenges that lie ahead and massive problems that still need solving. Fossil fuels are still our primary source of energy. People are still dying from disease and 11 percent of the world still doesn't have access to clean drinking water.[2] These issues are not just going to take care of themselves. People tend to forget how fragile this life is. Humans have only been on this planet for the blink of an eye, and if we're not careful, we will be gone in the next blink. We need creative and motivated people like you to tackle the issues of tomorrow and steer the collective rudder of humanity into a more productive and sustainable future.

---

[2] World Health Organization and UNICEF. "Progress on Drinking Water and Sanitation: 2012 Update. External." https://www.who.int/water_sanitation_health/publications/jmp_report-2012/en/.

Reason 2: Destroy the Stereotype. Given the magnitude of humanity's future obstacles, we will need every engineer, scientist, and innovator we can get. I want to destroy the stereotypes that deter potential students and demonstrate that anyone with a functioning brain and a strong will to improve can earn a degree any STEM discipline. There are far too many potential students who love science, technology, and problem-solving but never pursue higher education because they have bought into a false notion that they simply aren't capable. Most have come to believe that being a degreed engineer is some exclusive fraternity reserved for the ultra-smart and the intellectually gifted. Trust me, this is just not true.

The truth is that you do *not* have to be a genius to succeed in engineering or STEM. You do *not* need perfect genes or a high IQ. All you need is a strong belief that you *can* succeed and a willingness to improve yourself. I truly believe that anyone can do it, and I want my experience to serve as an example of how hard work and determination can bring average intelligence to a whole new level. Not the smartest kid in your school? Doesn't matter. GPA 0.1? Doesn't matter. If you want this badly enough, and you are willing to put in the work, you can get it. I wrote this book to show how it can be done. If you are willing to give what it takes, you can succeed no matter your background or academic history.

- -
The primary variables that will determine if you do or do not graduate have absolutely nothing to do with your IQ.
- -

Reason 3: You're Not Prepared for This. According to the American Society for Engineering Education (ASEE), you only have a 60 percent chance of graduating with a bachelor's degree in engineering. That's right, forty out of every one hundred freshmen will either drop out or switch majors, with twenty of those forty dropping out or switching majors their freshman year! When Las Vegas offers a comparable bet for your tuition money, we have a problem. These numbers are unacceptable to me. A process engineer would say that we need to increase our first pass yield!

The primary reason most students leave engineering school is not due to a lack of ability. It is due to a lack of preparation in the not-so-obvious areas that matter most. Most of which can be attributed to the demand chasm that exists between the average American high school curriculum and the average university engineering curriculum. This huge gap in expectations can leave even the most successful high school graduate feeling ill equipped and inadequate. This book was written to address these core needs that so many young students lack.

The Seven Fundamentals for Success

In the chapters ahead, you will find the essential pieces for your foundation of success. Regardless of your specific field of study, building this foundation is absolutely essential. Whether you're majoring in electrical, chemical, mechanical, computer, software, civil, mining, nuclear, or anything between. The fundamentals are the same and overarch all engineering and STEM (Science, Technology, Engineering, Math) disciplines. In sequential order of need, these seven fundamentals are:

1. Motivation
2. Self-discipline
3. Time creation and management

4. Sustainable lifestyle and schedule
5. Efficiency in everything
6. Studying and effective learning
7. Exam performance

These are the seven crucial areas that cause 99 percent of all student heartache. Ask any current or former engineering student. An honest assessment of their struggles would reveal a deficiency in at least one of the above seven areas. Believe me, I wish someone had taught me this when I was just starting. It would have saved me *a lot* of pain, stress, and time—and a few sobbing-in-the-fetal-position sessions. I want to help you become one of the few to avoid learning these lessons the hard way.

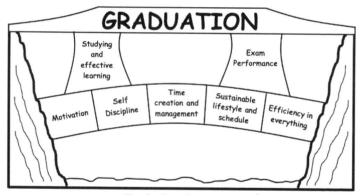

The Bridge of Graduation

You should view the seven fundamentals as shown in the above Bridge of Graduation. Studying performance and exam performance represent the two primary pillars that support your graduation. Those two pillars are supported by a foundation made from the remaining five fundamentals. Motivation, self-discipline, time, sustainability, and efficiency each serve as one piece in the foundation. Without just one of the pieces, the entire structure will fall.

This book will focus on these seven fundamentals because they are the root cause of low performance. If you think that technical skills like performing the triple integral of $\cos(x)\tan(yz)$ or determining the usable work of a combustion engine are what cause students to leave engineering, you're dead wrong. While specific skills like this are very important, they are not at the core of most students' struggles. So, if you're looking for help with specific technical material, there are countless textbooks ready and waiting at your school's bookstore. However, if you want to avoid the obstacles that account for the large majority of student pain and difficulty while setting yourself up for sustained success throughout your college career, keep reading.

Who This Book Is For

Are you interested in studying science, technology, engineering, or math (STEM)? Are you a college freshman who has no idea what you're doing but is eager to learn? Are you a high school student who wants to get a head start on your degree? Are you a current college student who is thinking about switching to an engineering or STEM degree? Are you a current student who is struggling, beaten down, and thinking about quitting? If you answered yes to any of these questions, this book is for *you*.

You've Come to the Right Place

If you wanted to compete in an Ironman triathlon, you wouldn't ask your ten-year-old niece to be your coach. If you wanted to know how to bake the perfect apple pie, you wouldn't ask your mechanic for baking tips. And if you wanted to learn how to treat that weird rash on your back, you wouldn't ask your mailman for a diagnosis. If you want to know how to do something, you find someone with the applicable corresponding experience. For an Ironman, you hire a triathlete coach. For baking tips, you ask your grandma. And for that rash on your back, you better visit your doctor. Pretty simple, right? When you want to know how to do something, you look for someone who has the experience. When it comes to succeeding in engineering school, I have that experience.

Throughout my academic career, I have personally experienced the full spectrum from failure to success. I know how inadequate you feel when you fail a course. I know what it's like to have your ego shattered when you get the lowest exam score. And I know what it feels like to question your own intelligence to the point of having one foot out the door. However, I also know how great it feels to get the highest exam score. I know how fulfilling it is to earn a report card of straight As. And I know what it's like to have the confidence to succeed in any course. But most importantly, I know the path between these two extremes. I know what needs to be learned and what is required to come back from those devastating setbacks. I know what changes are essential to developing sustained success. The topics in this book are based upon real scientific research, my own experience, and numerous interviews with other graduates, professors, and advisors. This book is the collection of crucial and overlooked information that I and many others wish we had from the beginning. A true road map from the bottom to the top. Rest assured; you have come to the right place.

TWO

So You Want to Be an Engineer

The engineer has been, and is, a maker of history.
—James Kip Finch

Welcome to the Path Less Traveled

Before we get down to business, I want to congratulate you for considering engineering as your career. It is undoubtedly a challenging undertaking and a choice that is not easy to make. However, the rewards and opportunities that will come with a degree in engineering are well worth the effort. Engineers are paid to combine science with creativity on a daily basis and play a vital role in the progression of society. This high degree of responsibility is only matched by the personal fulfillment an engineer feels after his or her work becomes successful. I can tell you from experience that one of the most satisfying things in this world is to watch an idea transform from just a single thought into a tangible reality. It's like magic! It's almost like watching your own child become successful on their own. I believe humans have an instinctual need for this kind of fulfillment, to be both creative and useful to society. Engineering can provide this fulfillment for you.

What Do We Do?

The more appropriate question would be, What *don't* we do? Engineers are involved in almost every major industry on the planet: agriculture, aerospace, transportation, infrastructure, pharmaceutical, computing, software, defense, energy, entertainment, food, health care, mining, communications, and environmental protection. The list goes on and on. Engineers are quite literally responsible for almost everything you interact with on a daily basis—the huge buildings we work in, the microscopic processing chips in our phones, the ultrasound machines that scan our bodies for infection, the medicine we take to feel better, the planes we fly in, and the software used to stop your car if you are in danger. All of these things are made possible by engineers. Basically, if it's created by humans, an engineer had a part in its design, manufacture, and testing. As you may imagine, the potential career possibilities are almost endless. Below is a list of just some of those careers.

Mechanical Engineer: Applies thermodynamics, fluid dynamics, strengths, and computer science to design and analyze mechanical systems.

Process Engineer: Applies reliability and optimization principles to manufacturing processes to maximize efficiency.

Chemical Engineer: Applies chemistry, physics, and biology to develop and produce useful chemicals and processes.

Electrical Engineer: Applies physics and computer programming to develop and test electrical systems and equipment.

Software Engineer: Applies mathematics, optimization, and programming to develop computer software and automation.

Systems Engineer: Oversees the design and integration of several engineering subsystems into one larger interdisciplinary system.

Project Engineer: Manages the development and production of a full product line or implementation of processes.

HVAC Engineer: Oversees the design, installation, and maintenance of heating and cooling systems.

Quality Engineer: Verifies that products are being designed and manufactured to the applicable standard or engineering drawing.

Reliability Engineer: Applies statistics and optimization techniques to analyze and predict product and equipment life span and maintenance schedules.

Biomedical Engineer: Applies chemistry, biology, and mechanics to produce artificial body parts and machines to diagnose medical issues.

Materials Engineer: Applies chemistry and material science to develop and analyze useful materials.

Mining Engineer: Develops equipment and systems to safely and reliably extract materials from the earth.

Nuclear Engineer: Develops processes and tools derived from nuclear energy and radiation.

Aerospace Engineer: Combines propulsion, flight mechanics, and control systems to produce effective vehicles and delivery systems.

Civil Engineer: Utilizes physics and strengths to develop and maintain building structures and urban infrastructure.

Manufacturing Engineer: Develops tools and processes to efficiently manufacture products.

Test Engineer: Develops tests required to verify the proper performance of a system or product.

Industrial Engineer: Applies statistics and data management to recognize trends and increase productivity and efficiency.

Field Engineer: Repairs and maintains products and equipment in a variety of locations all over the world.

Controls Engineer: Develops software and equipment to control larger systems and machinery.

Sustainability Engineer: Develops systems and processes to be more environmentally sustainable and energy efficient.

As you can see, the options are extensive, and this is by no means an exhaustive list. You would be very hard pressed to find a degree choice that offers more variety in the job market. But if you're in need of additional incentive, here are a few other reasons to feel good about your choice:

High Demand: The demand for new engineers continues to be strong. According to the ASEE, the demand for STEM graduates will continue to increase by 9 percent over the next ten years.

Transferable: The need for engineers is truly worldwide. You would be hard pressed to find a career that is more transferable between states and countries.

Prestige: Having an engineering degree will bring admiration from the people around you. You will be respected as someone who can tackle difficult problems and be trusted with a high degree of responsibility.

Fulfilling Work: The nature of an engineer's job is to improve the world around them by using their technical skills and imagination. It's easy to feel good about what you do when your ideas directly translate to real-world improvement.

Compensation: Money has the power to bring freedom and stability to your life and the lives of your family and loved ones. There is absolutely nothing wrong with letting it motivate you, especially when you find out that the current average salary for an engineer in the United States is $97,565.[3]

---

[3] US Bureau of Labor Statistics. "May 2019 National Occupational Employment and Wage Estimates." Last modified March 31, 2020. https://www.bls.gov/oes/current/oes_nat.htm.

- -
I can tell you from experience that one of the most satisfying things in this world is to watch an idea transform from just a single thought into tangible reality.
- -

Engineering Is in Your Blood

The ability to simply *imagine* and *create* sets humans apart from all other life on earth. We are unparalleled when it comes to continuous improvement and innovation. We are always progressing, stretching our limits, and never accept the current state of things for long. We are always questioning and analyzing our environment for possible improvements. We are always asking, "How could this be done better, faster, and more efficiently?" This type of thinking has enabled us to create the world we know today. Think back to how people lived only one hundred years ago—no vehicles, no cell phones, no internet, no satellites, no space exploration, no GPS, no computers, no antibiotics, and no commercial flight. That is a *huge* leap forward in just one lifetime. Progress like this would not be possible if engineering and innovation were not ingrained in our genetic code. Engineering is in our blood. In *your* blood.

History of Engineering

Warmth, protection, and the ability to cook food are the three things that gave the human race what it most needed, which was time. Once humans discovered how to reliably create fire, we no longer needed to spend our days just surviving as most animals do. Having warmth, protection, and cooked food on

22

demand really freed up some time in the days of early humans. Time that could be spent thinking of ways to continue improving. The more things were created and discovered, the more time we had to strengthen our minds and the less time we had to spend on survival. This consistent ingenuity allowed our species to create the world we live in today.

Rooted in those humble beginnings, the creative application of science and mathematics became known as engineering and the people who practiced these things became known as engineers. Since the beginning, engineers have produced countless creations and innovations that have contributed significantly to human progression—things like the wheel, the plow, the compass, the fastener, irrigation, optical lenses, antiseptics, the printing press, concrete, steel, batteries, light bulbs, and transistors. With each new innovation, endless doors opened to more innovation and progression. More and more engineers and innovators began to take up the call of progress. The list is long and includes names like Nikola Tesla (AC current electricity supply), Thomas Edison (light bulb and motion picture camera), Marie Curie (radioactivity), Alexander Graham Bell (telephone), Henry Ford (mass-produced vehicles), Charles Babbage (computer), Wright brothers (airplane), Thomas Savery (steam engine), and Alexander Fleming (penicillin). These innovators changed the course of history with their work. Their creations inspired new generations and paved the way for modern-day engineers and innovators to build upon their progress.

Modern-Day Engineering

Today, engineers have continued to push the boundaries of human capability. We are building skyscrapers over three-thousand feet tall. We can manipulate the genetic code of organisms. We launch rockets into space almost weekly. We can communicate with anyone anywhere in the world almost instantaneously. We can control machines with just our thoughts. We can 3D print almost anything. We carry the entirety of human knowledge in our pockets. We have vaccines for several deadly diseases. We have robots that can remotely perform surgery. And we can travel anywhere in the world in less than a day. These incredible advancements in science and technology have been made possible by current engineers and innovators. People like Elon Musk, who is revolutionizing the transportation, energy production, and space travel industries; Steve Jobs, who effectively put the internet in our pockets; and Jeff Bezos, who has revolutionized how we consume goods. These men are joined by thousands of other men and women engineers and innovators revolutionizing our world at an accelerating rate. Human progress has truly become exponential. It is astonishing to think about how far we have come in the past one hundred years. And what will be even more astonishing is where we will be one hundred years from now.

The Future of Engineering

It won't be long before the cutting-edge technology and engineering of today will be considered out of date and obsolete, mere stepping-stones on the never-ending path of progress. Before we know it, the emerging fields of today like bioengineering, automation, quantum computing, artificial intelligence, robotics, nanotechnology, genetic engineering, renewable energy, and virtual reality will dominate our everyday lives. Today, these technologies and markets are still in their infancies. It will be up to you and your peers to help them grow and mature.[4]

---

[4] There is a great website called www.engineeringchallenges.org, which lists the future engineering challenges that are considered the most important for us to solve. I highly recommend checking it out.

It is clear that the need for motivated and skilled engineers has never been greater. The future is inherently uncertain and will come with substantial challenges. These challenges will need to be met with proportional amounts of ambition and ingenuity. The ideas and innovations of the future need motivated and creative minds like yours to get off the ground, so I hope you are up to the task. Future generations will depend on it.

There is no doubt that the future holds great opportunity. It's like a blank canvas waiting to be filled in with your ideas and creativity or like the Wild West waiting to be settled. Everything you see started as just an idea. A single thought that grew into reality. The future is where your ideas will come to life. An engineering or STEM degree is the first step to this future of creativity, opportunity, and fulfillment. Consider this your official welcome to this wonderful world called engineering.

THREE

FINDING YOUR WHY

In order to accomplish anything, the strength of your
motive must match the difficulty of your goal.

Your Motive

Action requires energy. More specifically, the magnitude of
any action must be matched by the magnitude of the energy
supplied. If the supply of energy runs out before the action is
complete, the action will not happen. For example, if you try
to drive one hundred miles in your car with only fifty miles
worth of fuel, you're only going fifty miles, plain and simple.
Big actions require big energy. Engineering school is a big
action. Therefore, the energy required to graduate is also big.
Where is your energy going to come from? If you answered,
"Thousands of energy drinks and a constant IV drip of coffee," you're missing the point. I am talking about your motive—your reason and your *why*. Your motive for pursuing
engineering will be the *source* of your energy. It will be what
gets you through the late nights, the long weekends, and the

inevitable setbacks. Your motive will be what drives you through to graduation. It's needless to say that your motive is extremely important and the undeniable starting point in the foundation of your success.

The rest of this book will focus on the *how* of becoming successful in engineering school. But first, we need to discuss the *why*. Without a powerful motive, you can easily find yourself in a one-hundred-mile race with only fifty miles' worth of fuel. So it's only logical that we begin this journey with an evaluation of your motive. Let's begin by addressing some possible preconceptions you may have about what motives should or should not be.

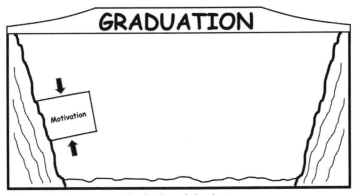

The Bridge of Graduation

It's Okay if It's Money

Before we go much further, I think this is a good time to address the elephant in the room—money. Yes, that necessary rectangular paper that we all need to survive and would love to have a swimming pool full of. Cue the mental image of Scrooge McDuck swimming in a vault of gold coins. Some other sources would tell you that money is not a worthy motivator for pursuing engineering or that the pursuit of a healthy salary is not a noble enough cause. I think that is totally ridiculous! A high salary is a completely acceptable motivation for becoming an engineer. In fact, a very large percentage of the students I've spoken with defined money as their primary motivation for pursuing an engineering degree, so do not feel guilty or selfish if your desire for a solid paycheck is what brought you here. Currently, the average household income in the United States is $60,293.[5] In 2019 the average salary for an engineer was $97,565.[6] That means that the average engineer on his or her own earns 50 percent more than an average household in the United States. I'd say that's pretty respectable and would be motivating for almost anyone.

However, if money is your motivation, I think it's important that you dig a little deeper and ask yourself, "Why do I want more money?" Everyone wants more money. But it is what you plan to do with that money that is your real motivator. This is what you need to define. Wanting money for the sake of having more money is probably not a motive that will get you through what lies ahead. Your motive needs to be a little more refined. Money is just a tool. And tools only become useful once they are used to create something. You should try to define what you plan to create with your money. For instance, during my research for this book, I spoke with a junior in electrical engineering whose primary motivator was money. When asked why he wanted more money, he laid out his very detailed plans to become a real estate investor and retire early so he could spend time with his family. His true

---

[5] US Census Bureau. "Quick Facts." https://www.census.gov/quickfacts/fact/table/US/SEX255218.

[6] US Bureau of Labor Statistics. "May 2019 National Occupational Employment and Wage Estimates." Last modified March 31, 2020. https://www.bls.gov/oes/current/oes_nat.htm.

motive was not simply having more money. It was his desire to have more free time with his family. Money just serves as the avenue to get him where he really wants to be. If your motive is to have more money, that is perfectly acceptable. But you should try to specifically define what you plan to *do* with more money because this will be your actual motive.

Your Motive Must Be Genuine

It doesn't matter what your motive is as long as it is genuine. If your motive isn't genuine, it's not going to produce very much energy. What motivates your parents, classmates, or siblings may not work for you. Don't try to project their motives onto yourself. This behavior will only lead to you not getting what you truly want. The right motive for you is the one that *actually* motivates you. It should be something that you find yourself thinking about every day without even trying—something that you just can't shake and is always in the back of your mind nagging at you and pushing you to perform.

After speaking with countless students about their motives for pursuing engineering school, I've noted that one thing is clear. There is no right or wrong motive. What motivates you is as individual as your favorite food. Everyone's is different. The main point I want to make here is that you shouldn't feel like your motive for becoming an engineer has to be anything that it is not. Don't feel guilty if your motive isn't to solve world hunger. It doesn't matter what it is. The only requirement is that it's genuine and strong—very strong.

Strength Matters

When I was young, I remember listening to the song "Tiny Dancer," by Elton John, on the radio. The music sounded so beautiful, and I imagined how cool it would be to play the piano like Elton. A few weeks later, I began piano lessons and never looked back. I stuck with them for the next twenty years and can now play beautifully. In fact, I can play every song by Elton John, and I have composed several original pieces of my own…just kidding! My lessons lasted about a month. The piano was hard! Especially during the summer when there were so many fun things I could be doing outside. So I quit. I truly did want to play the piano like Elton John. But I didn't want it badly enough to sacrifice the other things I wanted to do. What I really wanted was the ability to play the piano to be uploaded to my brain, like when Neo learned kung fu in *The Matrix.* When push came to shove, my motive was not strong enough, plain and simple. If my motive was strong enough, I would have had the energy to stay committed when temptation came knocking. In the end, I did not fail because I lacked ability. I failed because I lacked a strong motive. I simply didn't want it badly enough.

Now, when it came to an engineering degree, I wanted that more than anything. I was truly willing to sacrifice and put in the work necessary for success. As Yoda would say, "The motive is strong with this one." My desire to prove that I could succeed in the engineering arena was stronger than my desire to do anything else. I had no idea where I wanted to work, what I wanted to do, or if I would even graduate. All I knew was that I wanted to see what I was truly capable of. My desire to succeed was stronger than any amount of pain or sacrifice required for success. There were times in school when I felt as dumb as a rock. I experienced failures that left me feeling like I had surely missed a few grades somewhere. But when it came down to it, the thought of quitting school was always far worse. And that's what is important. That is the lesson here. The thought of not getting what you want must *always* be worse than any amount of work, stress, or sacrifice that your goals demand of you. That is how you know if your motive is strong enough.

The thought of not getting what you want must always be worse than any amount of work, stress, or sacrifice that your goals demand of you.

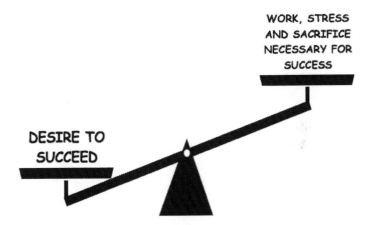

The strength of your motive will determine how much energy can be drawn from it. Engineering school is a big action that is going to require big energy. Not only will you need large amounts of energy to learn new and complex material, do homework daily, work on projects, study for exams, and attend lectures, but you will need even more energy to pick yourself up after setbacks and to deny temptation. After a failure, you will feel mentally, physically, and emotionally defeated. Your mind will go into survival mode and will push you to flee the premises and never return. There will be other times when a weekend out with friends or with your favorite video game sounds so much better than studying. It is especially during moments of failure and temptation when a different major starts to look very appealing. That's why it is so important that your motive be strong. During these times, your motive will be your last line of defense. And it needs to hold. It needs to always be there, nagging at you, getting you to class, keeping you on track, helping you stay up to study, and lifting your spirits after every setback. It needs to say, "Pick yourself up and move! We have a goal to accomplish!" Your motive needs to act as your internal compass, constantly pushing you in the direction of your goals.

The True Cause of Failure

I want you to think back to the last time you failed at something. Maybe it was an exam, a game, or weight loss. Now ask yourself why you failed. What was the underlying reason? Was it because you just weren't smart enough, talented enough, or skilled enough? Was your failure caused by you hitting the absolute limit of your abilities? If you answered *yes*, I want you to ask yourself this follow-up question. What if I was offered one billion dollars to succeed? Would I have found a way? Of course you would have found a way! A billion bucks is pretty damn motivating! All of a sudden, the excuse of "I'm not skilled, smart, or talented enough" just went out the window. We both know that for a billion dollars, you would've done what it took to succeed. This shows that you are truly capable of anything as long as there is a strong enough motive pushing you. I believe that way too many people assume that they are lacking in talent and ability. In reality, they are actually lacking in motivation. Without a strong motive, the energy to succeed just won't be there, and goals will remain goals.

People don't fail because they've hit their physical and mental limits. They fail because they don't put in the work necessary for success. *Never* blame your failures on things you can't change. Instead, always blame failure on your preparation. Because preparation can *always* be improved. The truth is you *are* capable of success in anything. We all are. You need to be willing to admit this truth to yourself. It can be a painful admission because it will eliminate all of the easy excuses for failure. But it's so important because it is the first step to true achievement. The sky's the limit! You must believe that if you want it badly enough, you will be willing to invest the time and energy required to learn, improve, and develop yourself until you get what you want. *Know this.*

Never blame your failures on things you can't change. Instead, always blame failure on your preparation. Because preparation can always be improved.

Define Your Motive

Hopefully, by now you have put some thought into what is specifically driving you toward an engineering degree. But if you haven't, take a moment and ask yourself the following question: "What is my reason for pursuing an engineering degree?" Or maybe a better way to ask this is, "What does an engineering degree give me that makes it worth doing over all other degrees?" For me, the answer was threefold:

Genuine Interest in the Material: Science and engineering have always intrigued me. I wanted to know more!

Fulfillment: Accomplishing something that is truly challenging is one of the most fulfilling things in this world. I wanted that fulfillment.

Paid Well to Be Creative: Engineering offered me the unique opportunity to be paid well while also fueling my creative fire.

What about you? What is your answer? Hopefully, it comes to you fairly quickly. But if it doesn't, you should take some time to really think about it and get to the bottom of what is pushing you down this road. Here are some examples of common motives for pursuing engineering school:

⇒ High variety in career options
⇒ Large salary
⇒ High job security
⇒ Very transferrable (engineers are needed everywhere)
⇒ Impact on family life
⇒ Interest in a specific topic
⇒ Challenge of the education itself
⇒ Prestige of being an engineer

All of these are equally valid motives, capable of carrying a student through to graduation. Maybe your motive is on the list, and maybe it's not. Again, all that matters is that it is genuine and strong. However, it is very important for you to define it. By defining your motive, you will bring a lot of clarity and simplicity to this endeavor. Then, once you do have your motive or motives (it's okay if you have more than one) defined, it's a good idea to write it down along with your other goals and post it somewhere that you'll see every day. This will bring your motive out into the open where it can live and become even more powerful.

PRO TIP: Post your goals. There is a very real power that comes from writing your goals down and looking at them daily. When you bring your goals out of your mind and into the real world, they can live, grow, and hold you accountable. Even if it's just on a Post-it note on your bathroom mirror, it's a simple yet very effective little trick that may surprise you. For maximum results, make sure each goal is well defined, easily measurable, and has a time component.

Bad example: *Do better in school.*

Good example: *Increase my GPA to at least 3.4 by the end of my sophomore year.*

Once you've accomplished a goal, don't forget to reward yourself. You deserve it! Treat yourself to a night out or buy that cool new thing you've been wanting. Nothing feels better than crossing off a goal from your list. Be sure to take advantage of this easy technique. It has worked wonders for me.

The Learning Curve Is Steep

So why is it important that your motive be strong? Well, engineering school is extremely demanding. You already know this. But there is a big difference between knowing something and *knowing* something. I'm talking about the type of knowledge that comes with experience. This lack of experience-derived knowledge is why most students are not mentally prepared for the demands of engineering school. Most high schools are just not setting the proper precedent, specifically for engineering students. Imagine preparing for a marathon, which is 26.2 miles, and your coach tells you that you're ready after your first 3-mile jog. This is essentially what is expected of incoming engineering freshmen going from the typical high school curriculum into the college engineering curriculum.

The demand gap is so considerable that it's no wonder freshmen engineering students become overwhelmed rather quickly. Being overwhelmed leads to stress. Stress leads to sadness. Sadness leads to anger. Anger leads to hate. And we all know that hate leads to the dark side! This huge gap in preparation and expectations is what this book will attempt to address.

The difficulty of engineering school can be split into the following three categories: mental, lifestyle, and schedule.

DIFFICULTY OF ENGINEERING SCHOOL

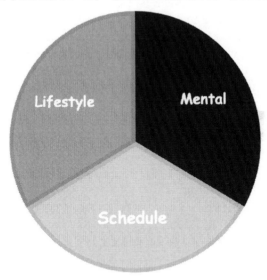

Mental: The mental difficulty of engineering school comes in two forms. The first simply comes from the complex material you will be engaging. High-level math and science topics can be quite abstract and will require some extra effort and time to absorb. The second form, and perhaps the biggest challenge for most students, is the large amount of mental stamina engineering school requires. A typical student should expect 20 to 30 hours of study time per week outside of class. This time can also increase significantly leading up to exams, which are typically held three to four times per semester per course. To be able to maintain this large amount of quality study time for four to five years requires students to develop a very high level of mental stamina. This will be explored further in the next chapter.

Schedule: Success in engineering school requires a very strict schedule with plenty of time reserved for studying. Prior to starting school, most students have some amount of obligation requiring some percentage of their weekly time. Typically, students will fit school into their already existing schedules and just hope things work out. Spoiler alert—it usually doesn't work out. What does your schedule currently look like? If you already have a busy schedule filled with work, family, friends, boyfriends, girlfriends, and other obligations, squeezing in engineering school can be next to impossible. A thorough analysis of your schedule and priorities must be performed before you begin. This topic is further addressed in chapter 5.

Lifestyle: Engineering school requires a lifestyle of commitment to your studies. This lifestyle change can be very difficult for some students to make. Prior to starting school, students will typically have things they like to do daily. Things like hanging with friends, video games, exercise, TV, and lounging. When school begins, much of the time spent doing these things may need to decrease or be sacrificed altogether. This can be a very difficult accommodation to make, so it is important that you understand the magnitude of what you are trying to accomplish and adjust your lifestyle accordingly. This topic is further addressed in chapter 6.

Do not let the last several paragraphs discourage you. Their purpose was not to scare you but to provide you with accurate expectations. The goal is to properly prepare you for what is to come. Imagine if someone gave you a jawbreaker and made you believe it was a gummy bear. Ouch! You would be fairly angry with that person. I want to prepare you for the reality of what you're taking on. You're getting a jawbreaker, plain and simple. Yes, the learning curve is steep. But as long as you are well prepared for the challenge, engineering school has the unique potential to mold you into a much better version of yourself.

The Weathered Tree

At this point, you may be feeling a little fearful or apprehensive about what lies ahead. Don't worry; most students feel this way in the beginning. I know I did, and rightfully so. The undertaking of engineering school can be quite daunting. But I want to convince you that difficulty should not be feared or avoided, but sought out and embraced instead. A challenge like engineering school should excite you and even motivate you further. Let me illustrate with an example.

Imagine two trees: one that is in a protected greenhouse and another that is outside and exposed to the elements. The tree in the greenhouse is watered on a regular daily schedule and is constantly protected from the wind, rain, and weather. The tree outside is left to develop on its own. It only drinks when it rains and has no protection from the elements. Over time both trees grow almost equally and appear very similar. But which tree do you think grew stronger? Which tree would you bet on to withstand 100 mph winds or to endure a drought? If you guessed the outside tree, then you're correct. It is well known that trees respond proportionally to what their environment throws at them. If there is not enough water, their roots spread out deeper and wider until they find moisture. If strong winds threaten their stability, they will compensate by becoming stronger and more flexible. The more stress they encounter, the more resilient they become.

39

Freshman you   Senior you

I make the above analogy to demonstrate the importance of not shying away from difficulty and stress. Your ability to endure and overcome is directly proportional to what you have already endured and overcome. As you face more and more challenges in your life, you will become stronger and more equipped to face future challenges. Your perception of what is difficult will evolve. What you once thought was challenging will now seem par for the course.

This idea can be further illustrated by revisiting the marathon training example. Once you begin training for a marathon, five miles will seem like a very challenging distance. After you actually run that first five miles, your perception of its difficulty decreases because you have actually accomplished the task. From then on, every time you run five miles, your perception of its difficulty decreases more and more. The distance that you now define as difficult increases, maybe up to ten miles. This cycle continues to fifteen miles, then twenty miles, and eventually reaches the full marathon distance. At this point, the distance is no longer terrifying for you. It has become a reasonable challenge. Running 26.2 miles is an insane undertaking to most of the world, but not for you. You have successfully trained your body and mind to be able to overcome this huge challenge. As a result, you now have a new perception of what you are capable of. Your limits have expanded.

Perhaps the best part about accomplishing these types of large challenges is that their benefits will translate across all areas of your life. What you once thought was a difficult undertaking at work is now not so daunting. What you once thought was a huge project at home is now not so overwhelming. And what you once thought was unachievable in the gym is now actually attainable. The benefits are everywhere. Your perception of what is actually difficult will change for everything. Your mental capability to process and break down large tasks will increase. You will not become overwhelmed as easily and you will be able to efficiently dissect large intimidating tasks into smaller bite-size chunks. Because now, through your experience, you will know that these huge tasks are actually possible to complete. This characteristic will make you a much more valuable asset to any employer and, more importantly, to yourself.

So the fact that engineering school is very difficult should not scare you. It should motivate you. This is the type of challenge that can really transform you into a more confident and robust version of yourself—one that can truly open your eyes to what you are capable of doing. Things that you once thought were out of your realm of accomplishment will now be viewed with hungry eyes. You should be looking for challenges like this. Because they have the potential to improve you as nothing else can. The overarching benefits of accomplishing a task of this magnitude are priceless.

Quick Recap

The path to your degree begins with your motive. It is why you are reading this book! It is the reason you are on this path. It will be your source of energy on the journey ahead. The strength of your motive must be proportional to the challenge of engineering school. Whatever motivates you must warrant the time, energy, stress, sacrifice, and money required for success. Whether it be the many careers that are available, the healthy paycheck, the prestige of the title, or the freedom to live almost anywhere, the force that has driven you here must be a strong one. Because one thing is for certain—engineering will test you. It will challenge you in ways that you have never experienced before. It will demand your absolute best. It will require you to expand yourself in ways that you never thought possible. But above all, it will mold you into a more durable and robust person who is capable of so much more than you are now. Your motive is the catalyst toward that better version of you.

FOUR

THE SECRET INGREDIENT

Self-discipline is the bridge between goals and
accomplishment.

Self-Discipline

In the previous chapter, we established that your energy will
derive from your motive. Now it's time to talk about where
all of that energy will go. Your car needs more than just gas
to move forward; it also needs an engine. Self-discipline is
your engine. Your motive provides the energy, and self-discipline provides work. It is the single most important attribute
that an engineering student can develop—not only for success
in school but for success in life as well. Self-discipline will
pave the way to accomplishing any goal you may have.
Whether it be in your career, physical health, relationships, or
life in general. If you have goals that need accomplishing, developing self-discipline is priority number one.

Self-discipline is what separates the doers from the triers, the players from the spectators, and the haves from the have-nots. Motivation will put you on the correct path, but self-discipline is what actually moves you forward. It is the force that will get you to class day after day. And it will keep you on task in the face of distraction and temptation. In this chapter we will explore the incredible importance of self-discipline and how it can be developed and strengthened over time.

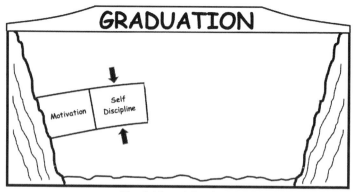

The Bridge of Graduation

How Self-Discipline Saved My Degree

It was the summer of my sophomore year. The spring semester had just ended, and school was not going well for yours truly. All I wanted was a break from the relentless grind so I could enjoy a normal, relaxing summer. But, unfortunately for me, I had just failed thermodynamics. And in order to stay on track, l had to retake it over the summer. At this point, school was getting pretty tiresome and no longer enjoyable. As the difficulty of my course load continued to increase, my inadequacies in studying and test-taking became more and more exposed. If I wasn't failing my courses, I was barely passing them. I was sick of feeling like I was constantly on the edge of total defeat. I felt like I was slowly but surely moving toward dropout lane. If something didn't change soon, I was going to lose this game. It was time to go for broke. That summer, I told myself that I was going to give it my absolute all and leave everything on the field. At the end of that summer, I wanted to be able to say that I honestly gave it my best effort.

I began by completely overhauling my approach. Thermodynamics became my absolute, undeniable, no-questions-asked, number-one priority. Everything else came second. Remember the "if someone offered you one billion dollars" scenario from earlier? That's exactly what I did. I acted as though someone offered me one billion dollars to pass thermodynamics. I comprehensively changed how I studied, completed homework, approached lectures, and took exams. Instead of just memorizing how to solve a few problems my professor highlighted in class, I learned the core theory and fundamentals that governed those problems. If I didn't understand something during the lecture, I raised my hand with questions until I understood. I actually *read* the textbook. Crazy, right? I read and reread every dang word until I absorbed and understood the information. If I struggled with a particular topic, I would immediately email the teacher's assistant (TA) or follow up with my professor the next class day. I would block out several days of study time prior to every exam. I took the homework much more seriously, spending as much time as it took until I knew it was correct. Studying became a daily habit instead of something I did the night before exams. I was not going to have an excuse if I failed this time.

That may seem like a lot of changes, but the previous paragraph can really be boiled down to one overarching theme. *I started exercising considerable self-discipline toward school.* That's it. I established a plan and attacked with massive amounts of discipline. The approach worked. I got an A- in the class, and it was one of the proudest moments of my life. I had proven to myself that I was capable of succeeding in the arena of engineering. My perception of my own capabilities totally changed. I now knew the recipe for success, and the secret ingredient was self-discipline.

The summer of my sophomore year was a total inflection point for me. Prior to that summer, I had failed four courses, and my GPA was a C+ average. After that summer my GPA increased to an A- average, and I never failed a course again. The content of this book is influenced in large part by what I learned and implemented over those few months, beginning with a large dose of self-discipline.

The Difference Maker

I want you to mentally list everyone you know that has ever said something like, "I have a great idea for a product or business!" or "It is my dream to become a_____" (fill in the blank) or "I would really like to get into better shape" or "I want to be a millionaire someday." You most likely have a pretty long list of people. Now, I want you to list everyone who actually accomplished the things they wanted. What does this new list look like? I think it is safe to assume that the second list is much smaller than the first list. The question is, Why? What is missing? Why didn't everyone get what they desired? You guessed it. The answer is that most people lack the self-discipline necessary to accomplish their goals. Self-discipline is *the* difference maker. It is the secret ingredient for success.

So if self-discipline is so powerful, why doesn't everyone have it? The answer is that most people don't like work. They don't like difficulty, and most of all, they don't like failure.

Developing strong self-discipline requires a large dose of all three. Thomas Edison captured this idea perfectly when he said, "Opportunity is often missed because it is disguised in overalls and looks like work." We all have big dreams. We all want a lot for ourselves. But when push comes to shove, most people end up settling for mediocrity. It is just simply easier. Hard work is just too…hard. Once people start to feel the grind or suffer a few setbacks, almost everyone quits or settles for less. Why do you think all of those get-rich-quick schemes and magic weight-loss pills sell so well? People want the results. but they don't want to put in the work. I hate to break it to you, but self-discipline is as close as you're going to get to a magic pill. You must take the time to cultivate it because it will push you through the work, the difficulty, and the setbacks. Self-discipline is the vehicle that can literally take you wherever you want to go.

- -

**Opportunity is often missed because it is disguised in overalls and looks like work.
—Thomas Edison**

- -

The Great Equalizer

When I first began taking engineering courses, I felt so out of place. It seemed like all of these other kids had been plugged into the engineering pipeline since they were breastfeeding. I felt like I didn't even deserve to be in the same room, and why would I? I didn't have an IQ over one hundred or come from a family of engineers. How could I possibly have any chance of success? Again, the answer is self-discipline. I hadn't taken math past algebra or studied longer than an hour in my life.

But what I did know was how to work hard and handle disappointment. This was good because, in the beginning, I failed several courses and rarely received anything above a C. What I lacked in raw smarts, I made up for with strong self-discipline. I didn't quit. I kept my head down and kept grinding. If my glass was filled with 10 percent raw mental talent, the remaining 90 percent was filled with self-discipline.

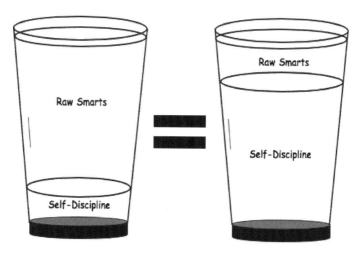

Over time it began to get easier; my performance improved, and my brain got stronger. I began to feel more like I belonged. It did not come easily, but the point is that, eventually, I did improve. My mental capabilities in comprehension and endurance strengthened. Eventually, I caught up with those other kids and actually surpassed many of them. Are you feeling like I did in the beginning? Maybe a little inadequate or like you don't belong? I'm here to tell you that you *do* belong. And you *can* succeed. What you may lack in raw talent or smarts can be compensated for with self-discipline. I am living proof that this is true. My strong self-discipline leveled the playing field. It didn't allow me to quit but pushed me to keep grinding until the results came. Self-discipline was my equalizer. And it will be yours as well.

Strengthening Your Brain with Neuroplasticity

What if I told you that I would pay you $200,000 per year if you could run fifty miles? Would you take me up on the deal? Sounds pretty reasonable, right? How would you go about conditioning your body to accomplish something like that? You'd probably start by getting your butt to the gym! It is scientifically proven and widely accepted that if we continually break down our muscles through frequent exercise, they will grow stronger and more capable over time. Everyone knows this, so the ability to run fifty miles is actually not that outlandish. We all know that if we put in the time and effort, our muscles will grow and improve. Eventually, we would be giving Sonic the Hedgehog a run for his money: $200,000 per year here we come!

"Wait a second, how is running going to help me get through school?" I'm so glad you asked! I want you to think of engineering school in exactly the same way as described in the above running example. Except instead of getting jacked leg muscles, you're strengthening your brain. And instead of running fifty miles, the goal will be to process complex topics and easily study for hours on end. You need to develop a new perspective of your own brain. You must realize that your brain's capabilities can be strengthened just like a muscle. Once you perceive your brain in the same way as a muscle, a world of new possibilities will appear.

The problem is that most people do not view the brain as something that can be strengthened. People think that we are born with a finite amount of mental capacity and that we just have to make do with what we've got. We have been led to believe that our IQ cannot be changed. Well, I'm here to tell you that that is *not true*! If you can take only one point away from this book, it should be this one. Your mental capacity to comprehend, process, and endure difficult tasks is *not* set in stone. It can be strengthened and improved through consistent mental stimulation and exercise, exactly the same way your muscles can. This incredible ability is made possible by something called neuroplasticity.

Neuroplasticity is how you will become more capable of tackling the material in engineering. As a certain area of the brain is used more and more, it compensates by creating new neural pathways and strengthening those that already exist. Over time this process makes it easier to form and retain new memories and increases your ability to comprehend new information. Isn't that wonderful? So do not worry if you currently struggle with math or if you can't focus on a textbook for longer than twenty minutes. These skills can be improved with consistent practice and proper mental stimulation. Think of the course material as your mental dumbbells and the amount of time you study as your mental treadmill. Before long, your brain will get the hint and begin to compensate. Just stick with it.

I personally experienced the incredible power of neuroplasticity, and it was remarkable. When I look back on my freshman year, I remember how difficult it was for me to process the concepts in precalculus and how torturous it was to sit down and study for longer than an hour. Then I compare this to the last year of my master's degree, when I was quickly processing advanced principles in aerodynamics and thermal system design while successfully studying for several days in a row without difficulty. After years of consistently challenging myself with difficult material and long hours of study time, my brain compensated and became stronger in the areas I needed it to—all thanks to neuroplasticity.

Now, before you get too excited, it is important for you to understand that strengthening your brain is not an overnight process. You're not going to read your entire math book and then wake up the next day feeling like Neil deGrasse Tyson. Developing those neural pathways will take time, dedication, and, above all, patience. But just like a muscle, with consistent training, big improvements can be made. Small progressive steps add up to big changes. The most important takeaway here is that you can improve your mental abilities. Your skills in comprehension and mental endurance *can* and *will* improve. But the only way is through strong self-discipline.

Your mental capacity to comprehend, process, and endure difficult tasks is *not* set in stone. It can be strengthened and improved through consistent stimulation and exercise.

Developing Self-Discipline through the Formation of Habits

Just like any other skill, self-discipline can be developed. It is a learned behavior that eventually becomes habitual, like brushing your teeth every morning or exercising daily. Once you get into a rhythm, it becomes a habit and therefore much easier to maintain. In fact, the act of forming new productive habits strengthens your self-discipline. And as your self-discipline becomes stronger, it will become easier to establish and maintain productive habits. Self-discipline is created and fed through productive habitual behavior. The Merriam-Webster dictionary defines self-discipline as "correction or regulation of oneself for the sake of improvement." This definition is actually the recipe for forming a new productive habit. You are correcting your unwanted behavior and regulating it until it becomes habitual.

Forming productive habits and developing self-discipline go hand in hand. You can't develop one without the other. By forming a new productive habit, you will strengthen your self-discipline. But the real question is how do you form that first productive habit if you don't have strong self-discipline to begin with? The rest of this chapter is dedicated to answering that question. It will provide tips, techniques, and systems that you can utilize to help in the formation of your first productive habit.

Set Yourself Up for Success

Developing self-discipline will take time. Say it with me, "Baby steps, baby steps, baby steps." You are teaching your mind and body a new default behavior, and it will not happen quickly. How do you eat an elephant? One small bite at a time. Many students learn this lesson the hard way. In an effort to get to graduation as fast as possible, students will take on way more than they can handle—signing up for four, five, or six classes thinking they're superhuman and that they just saved themselves a semester. I can't tell you how many times I have seen this bite people right in the butt. Not only do they perform poorly in their classes, but their self-confidence takes a huge hit as well. Trust me, two As are always better than three Cs and an F.

People can only take so much failure and defeat before it starts to really wear on them. This is why it is so important for you to avoid this type of situation. In order to successfully develop your own self-discipline, I recommend starting off slowly. Take on a course load that is challenging but you know you will be able to handle. The worst-case scenario is that it ends up being too easy and you ace everything. Your first few semesters should be used to develop the self-discipline and habits that will get you through the rest of your degree. Do not worry about how long it will take because it varies for everyone. A seven-year engineering degree is better than no degree at all. In fact, according to ASEE, only 34 percent of students graduate within four years.[7] As you sign up for classes, be realistic and ask yourself, "Can I honestly see myself succeeding with this course-load?" Always err on the conservative side, especially in the beginning. Your first few semesters should be used to build momentum and self-confidence. Remember, baby steps.

Daily Mental Exercise (Your First Habit)

The time has come for you to start forming the most important habit for academic success. Daily mental exercise. There are many other productive habits that will be discussed later in this book, such as physical exercise, proper sleep, and meditation. However, daily mental exercise will have the most immediate impact on your success, which is why I recommend starting with it. Let's begin by establishing a baseline.

In this case, your baseline will be how long you can study before your brain can no longer focus productively. Is it twenty minutes? Sixty minutes? Ninety minutes? Whatever your number is, it will be your baseline. It will be the daily

---

[7] American Society for Engineering Education. "Engineering by the Numbers: ASEE Retention and Time-to-Graduation Benchmarks for Undergraduate Engineering Schools, Departments and Programs." Washington, DC: Brian L. Yoder, 2016

amount of time that you will commit to studying, doing homework, or otherwise exercising your brain. Make sure you set a sustainable number, an amount of time that you can commit to on a daily basis. Don't worry about the "how" yet; we will go over study techniques in chapter 7. Right now, you are just establishing the habit. Remember, this is just a starting point. This is the foundation that you will build upon going forward, so it is very important that you do not overdo it. The time you set should be long enough to challenge your mental endurance but not exhaust you. This is all about consistency. New habits require consistent behavior to take hold. Assuming that your course load is appropriate, there should be a nice steady flow of difficult material. Which is exactly what you need to feed your new habit.

Forming the Habit

Is it difficult for you to brush your teeth in the morning? No, of course not. Brushing your teeth is just something you do without even thinking. It's a habit that has become so ingrained into your daily routine that you feel weird if you don't do it—the same feeling you get if you forget to put on underwear one day or don't put deodorant on. This is how your school work needs to be. It needs to become a part of your daily routine, so much so that you do not feel the mental resistance any longer. Remember, once the habit of mental exercise is formed, your brain will begin to compensate and grow stronger. Your mind needs to get used to being exercised and challenged consistently.

The latest studies show that it takes roughly sixty-six days to form a new habit.[8] Although it may be a bit longer or shorter

---

[8] Phillippa Lally, Cornella H. M. van Jaarsveld, Henry W. W. Potts, and Jane Wardle. "How Are Habits Formed: Modeling Habit Formation in the Real World." *European Journal of Social Psychology* volume 40, issue 6. (2009) pages 998-1009.

for you, it is extremely important that you not waver during this formation period. You are literally rewiring your brain. It is going to want to revert back to its prewired behavior, so you absolutely must stay on task. Think of your brain as a boat trapped in a whirlpool. In order to escape, the boat must turn its rudder fully and apply constant power. If the captain lets that rudder straighten for just a moment, the boat will be pulled straight back into the infinite cycle of the whirlpool. But once the boat has escaped, it is free to travel without resistance. Once you have firmly established the new habit, it will take much less willpower to maintain. Your new behavior will begin to feel more normal to you.

Below are some of the most effective and science-backed techniques that I recommend to create and maintain a new habit. All of these techniques helped me become more disciplined in school.

Habit Pairing: Think of all the daily habitual behaviors that you already have established. These might include brushing your teeth, taking a shower, making coffee, exercising, and walking the dog. Because these habits already have established time slots in your day, try scheduling your new desired habit directly after one of your established habits, thus pairing them together. I love this technique because it almost feels like you're not even creating a new habit. It just feels like you're expanding the habit that is already in place. The already established habit acts as your mental cue to begin the new behavior. For example, when I was trying to establish a daily habit of writing, I told myself that I would write for at least one hour immediately after I poured my morning coffee. I knew there was absolutely no way I wasn't drinking coffee every morning, so it could serve as a very consistent cue for my new desired habit of writing. On top of that, I knew the caffeine would enhance my ability to concentrate while writing. Double bonus points! When you pair habits together, it significantly cuts down on the willpower needed to execute the new behavior, therefore making it much easier to establish. I've had a lot of success with this technique, and I highly recommend it.

Automate Your Schedule: When forming a new habit, it is essential to minimize the amount of willpower needed to overcome your own objections. The easier you can make it on yourself, the better. Luckily for us, we live in a world of technology. There are all sorts of tools and apps ready and waiting to help you stay on track. Once you have established the daily time that you want to spend on your new habit, try setting a meeting in your phone's schedule. Also, make sure you set a reminder for that meeting. I actually like to set two reminders, the first for five minutes before and the second for the time of the event. You should then set this meeting to reoccur daily. This is a great way to establish a consistent reminder for yourself, which is particularly important on days when you're struggling.

Create Convenience: Humans absolutely love convenience. We love anything that makes our lives even just a little bit easier. That is why it is important to make performing your new habit as convenient as possible. Creating convenience means eliminating all of your potential excuses before they have the opportunity to derail you. For instance, when I was trying to establish a habit of regular exercise, I knew that I would eventually feel inconvenienced by having to drive to the gym every other day, which could have led to me missing some days. So I preemptively killed that excuse by investing in a small home gym. Now I can walk straight from my bed to the exercise room. It is so convenient that I no longer have an excuse to miss a workout. I suggest you do the same with your studying. Try to imagine your future self on days when you're less motivated. What excuses will you be coming up with? Remove the opportunity for those excuses to take hold before they derail you.

For example, many students enjoy studying at school, a coffee shop, or a library. These are all adequate places to study, but I don't recommend relying on these places for your daily study time. They require extra travel time and may not always be open. Why not take your favorite things about these places and implement them at home? Another idea would be to schedule your study time at the same time every day. A time when you know you will always be free. A time when there will be the least amount of potential distraction and alternative temptation. You know yourself better than anyone, so go through your own potential inconveniences and get rid of them now. Set yourself up for success by making the formation of your new habit as convenient as possible.

Visual Accountability: When I was in elementary school, I had trouble wearing my glasses every day. In an effort to help, my parents made a little chart with a box for every day of the week. In the middle of each box was a picture of me wearing my super awesome glasses. If I wore my glasses, I got to physically cross off that day on the calendar. If I made it through a whole month wearing my glasses, I was rewarded with dinner and a movie. This technique worked wonders for me. Once my goal moved out of the verbal world and into the physical world (i.e., a paper calendar), something changed for me. The goal became more real. I began to really enjoy crossing off the days when I wore my glasses. Being able to physically see my progress was very rewarding.

I still use this technique today. As I mentioned before, I set a goal to write at least one hour every day. Once I reach that goal, I physically mark it complete in my phone's planner. This technique is especially powerful once you really get rolling. Once you can physically see how much progress you've made on a calendar or chart, it becomes that much more painful to miss a day. It feels like you're betraying all of your past progress. I recommend implementing something similar for your goals. Something visual that you will see every day. This will not only provide you with a nice reminder but it will also provide you with a physical representation of your progress. The more visible it is, the better.

Tell People: If you live with roommates or a significant other, tell them what you're doing. The more people that know about your goals the better. Especially if they have the same goals as you. Maybe they can help keep you on track. We call these special friends "accountabili-buddies." We humans deal with failure much more easily if we're the only ones that know about it. But once other people are involved, the stakes get a little higher if you fail. Nobody likes disappointing other people. If you make your goals public, it will make accomplishing them that much more crucial.

Rewards: As important as it is to set goals, stay on track, and be accountable, it is equally important to establish an effective reward for your efforts. But be careful here—your reward for developing a new habit should not be taking a break from that new habit. This is how a lot of people slip up and fall off track. Instead, try to reward yourself with something that reinforces your new habit, something that helps you get even closer to your goals. In this case, maybe a new tablet might make sense, or a new home office, or a shiny new calculator!

Speaking of rewards, a good exam score can serve as a great reward in itself. The idea here is to establish a positive feedback loop for yourself. You put in the work, then that work translates to good grades. Rinse and repeat. It may take some time to determine how much work it takes for you to get the grades you desire, but be patient. It is a process. I didn't figure it out until I was almost halfway through school. But once those good grades started rolling in, I felt like a million bucks. It was all the reward I needed.

Maintaining Self-Discipline

It is vital that, once you begin to develop self-discipline with your studies, you maintain it year-round. The great thing about self-discipline is that it can be cultivated in many other areas of your life—exercise, diet, and skill development to name just a few. During summers and other breaks in school, I highly recommend continuing the development of your self-discipline by forming other productive habits. Get creative and make it fun. Have you been wanting to get in better shape? Get in control of your diet? Or become proficient in a new skill? Utilize these breaks in school to further the development of your self-discipline by unleashing it on something new. Remember that this is not a temporary change. You are not going to revert to your old self once this is done. This is a complete transformation. You are improving who you are at your core. It has been said that the purpose of having a goal is not just to achieve it but to become who you need to be in order to achieve it. Who you will become during this process is the real reward. By the end of school, you will not only be a disciplined student but a disciplined person.

- -

The purpose of having a goal is not just to achieve it but to become who you need to be in order to achieve it.

- -

Quick Recap

So maybe you weren't naturally gifted mentally. Maybe you weren't solving calculus problems at age seven. Maybe you're not the smartest kid in your class. Or you may even be well below average like I was. The good news is that none of that matters. Because there is a secret weapon, and it is available to anyone and everyone who is willing to develop it. It's called self-discipline. By cultivating and utilizing self-discipline, you can compensate for any mental weakness through the science of neuroplasticity. Similar to the development of new muscles, the brain's neural pathways and capability can be changed and strengthened over time. The first step should be to develop a strong habit of consistent mental exercise. Once established, your ability to form new memories and comprehend complex material will gradually increase. Before long, you will feel like you're drinking from a water fountain instead of a firehose. Self-discipline is your vehicle to graduation. Once you develop it, not only will you have a much easier time in school but you will have a much easier time accomplishing any goal throughout the rest of your life.

FIVE

FINDING TIME

No amount of money ever bought a second of time.
—Tony Stark

The Price of Time

Your education will require payment in two forms. Obviously, money is the first form and is relatively straightforward. Money pays for tuition, textbooks, supplies, parking, transportation, food, and housing. You already knew this—nothing new here. The second form, time, is less obvious and not nearly as well defined. Time is how you will pay for the actual knowledge you need to succeed. And unlike the financial cost of school, the amount of time required for success is not always a known quantity. It will change and fluctuate on a week-by-week, day-by-day, and student-by-student basis. But one thing is for certain: between lectures, studying, homework, labs, and projects, it will definitely not be zero—far from it, actually. For most full-time engineering students, the amount of time required for success is between twenty to fifty

61

hours per week, depending on the course load. Do you currently have this amount of free time available? I'm guessing the answer is probably not. This chapter can help with that.

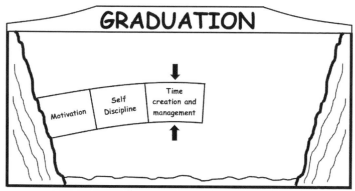

The Bridge of Graduation

Planning Ahead

It is essential that you dedicate a sufficient amount of time to school *before* you begin. The last thing you want is to be halfway through a semester and realize that you have way too much on your plate. That leads to the dark side, remember? Unfortunately, this scenario is all too common with new students. They come in thinking it will be just like high school and then get completely blindsided by the workload. They underestimate either how difficult the coursework will be, the sheer volume of work, or how much work they themselves can sustain throughout a semester. Either way, they pay the same price in poor performance and bad grades. Do not make this mistake.

The amount of time you dedicate to your studies should be viewed just like tuition—not optional. If you don't pay tuition, you will be kicked out of school. If you don't dedicate the necessary amount of time required for success, you will fail and be kicked out of school. You get the same result in both scenarios. Trust me on this one. The material and coursework will demand more time than you think it will, so it is vital that you plan ahead. Not just an hour here and there, but good quality chunks of time that are allocated specifically for studying and homework. This chapter will help you analyze where you spend your time so you can trim the fat and develop a successful schedule. And it all begins with a major priority shift.

Make School Your *First* Priority

The first step in creating more time for anything is making it a high priority. If you place more importance on all of your other nonschool activities, then it will be impossible to free up the amount of time necessary for success. In order for this to work, it is imperative that your education become your highest priority. Obviously, I'm not saying that you should let your relationships die just so you can pass calculus. All I am saying is that everything else on your schedule should be more flexible than your study time. Your study time should almost always be the last thing that either moves or changes. When you truly make something your first priority, it is remarkable how much easier it becomes.

I currently work with a senior in mechanical engineering whose current situation demonstrates this idea perfectly. His current life situation is as follows. He attends school full time (twelve credit hours); works full time (forty hours a week); has six children ages three, five, seven, ten, twelve, and fourteen; and is currently finishing the basement of his home. Oh, and to top it all off, he also lives forty-five minutes from school. From an outsider's perspective, this scenario seems like a recipe for disaster. And yet my friend holds a 3.2 GPA and is on track to graduate in two semesters. Yes, his marriage is healthy, and his children still have a father. What makes his success possible is that he has firmly established his studies as his clear number one priority. Everything else in his life adapts to his education—not the other way around. My friend's scenario serves as an example of how important and powerful prioritization can be. By defining clear priorities and acting on them, he is able to succeed in school despite his long list of obligations. I realize that this may seem like a subtle change, but, trust me, once you have firmly established school as your number one priority, your road to graduation will become much clearer.

The Time Budget

There are exactly twenty-four hours in each day. They are yours to be spent on whatever you deem worthy. Where do you currently spend your twenty-four? What does your average day look like? If you are anything like most college students, your time is mostly spent sleeping, working, and being leisurely. The average American college student's day is broken down and shown in the following table.

Activity	Time spent (hours)
Sleep	8.8
Leisure and sports	4
Education	3.5
Working	2.3
Other	2.2
Traveling	1.4
Eating and Drinking	1
Grooming	0.8

US Bureau of Labor Statistics 15-49 [9]

How does your average day compare? Over the next week, document your daily activities and roughly how much time you spend on each. You may be surprised where your time goes. Make sure to include everything: sleep, work, education, commute, exercise, gaming, social media, TV, cooking…you get the idea. Don't worry if it doesn't look like the example provided, and feel free to add as many different categories as needed. Just make sure the hours add up to exactly twenty-four and try to be as accurate as possible. This list will give you a good bird's-eye view of where your time goes every day.

---

[9] US Bureau of Labor Statistics. "American Time Use Survey." Last Modified December 20, 2016. https://www.bls.gov/tus/charts/students.htm

Once you have your list, organize it from top to bottom. From "most time spent" to "least time spent." What are your heavy hitters? And how much time are you currently spending on education? According to the data, the average student only spends about three and a half hours per day on education (remember, this includes both class time and study time). For you, this number will most definitely need to increase. This means one or several of your other daily activities will need to be either eliminated or altered to make room for your new priority.

True Value Test

The difficulty in changing your daily schedule comes in knowing what items are expendable. How do you know what items on your list can be removed or altered? This is where I like to use what I call the "true value test." True value is anything that contributes positively to your overall health or moves you in the direction of your goals. Move down the list and ask yourself if each activity is actually adding true value to your life. If the answer is no, then that activity is now on the chopping block. Another good way to clarify true value is to determine if your overall happiness has increased after completing an activity. Do you feel better or happier after the activity is complete? Things that come to mind for me here are exercise and writing. I always feel better once those things are done because they contribute directly to both my overall health and my goals. The key is to be truthful and objective. As long as you are honest with yourself, I have no doubt that you will find the waste in your day. Things that come to mind here are social media time and television. However, it's not always so simple. Many time consumers are rather difficult to change or eliminate. Especially things like work and transportation. That is why the rest of this chapter will focus on these hard-to-change activities.

Remember, the knowledge and stamina you need to succeed will require a lot of time to develop. Most students struggle because they do not dedicate an adequate amount of time to their schooling and mental development. In the pages ahead, it may feel like we are getting off topic and lost in the weeds. But don't lose focus of the core purpose here—less time spent doing other things equals more time freed up for school. The rest of this chapter aims to help you decrease your nonschool-time obligations.

Decreasing Time at Work

If you have a job, I want you to answer the following question. Why do you work? Let me guess—it's because you absolutely love what you do, and your happiness completely depends on you working forty to fifty hours per week? Am I right? I doubt it. The real answer is that you work because you need money. Just like everyone else. You may enjoy your job, but would you do it for free? Most likely not. Money puts food on the table, pays the bills, and keeps a roof over your head. Money is absolutely essential to survive in this society. If we're going to talk about decreasing the time you spend at work, then what we really need to talk about is decreasing how much money you need to live.

For instance, let's assume that you make $10 per hour (after taxes). This means that for every $10 you can cut from your monthly expenses, you will effectively free up one hour that would have been spent at your job and can now be dedicated to your studies. *The less money you need, the less time you need to spend at work.* It's that simple. So the focus should be on decreasing the reasons you need money. The rest of this section will be dedicated to ways you can save money and decrease your living expenses, beginning with the big three—housing, transportation, and education.

Higher monthly expenses = more time spent at work = less time spent studying.

Housing

According to the Bureau of Labor Statistics, the average American's largest monthly expense is housing.[10] Coming in at 33 percent of the average American's monthly income, that's a big chunk! By eliminating or decreasing your housing costs, you will substantially adjust the potential impact on your cost of living and therefore on your study time. Let's go through some of the best ways to do just that.

Stay at Home: The most effective way to decrease your housing costs is to not have any in the first place! If you are under thirty, then there is a good chance that your parents still have some room and tolerance for you at home. If your parents aren't an option, maybe you have some other family member who is willing to take you in while you're in school. While this may not be the "coolest" decision that you ever make, it will for sure be one of the smartest. Yes, it is true that the house gets smaller and smaller the older you get. The outside world will tug at you, and your friends may poke fun. But depending on where you live, the monthly savings will be around $900 in rent and utilities, which translates to *a lot* of

---

[10] US Bureau of Labor Statistics. "Consumer Expenditures—2018." Last Modified September 10, 2019. https://www.bls.gov/opub/reports/consumer-expenditures/2018/home.htm

time savings. Before you fall for the lure of having your own place, realize the impact it could have on your studies.

I have had many personal friends who have been seduced by the perceived freedom of their own house or apartment away from their families. When in reality, they now have less freedom because they are shackled to a new mortgage or rent payment, which directly translates to less time they can dedicate to their studies. Higher monthly expenses equals more time spent at work, which equals less time spent studying. In some cases, I have even seen friends drop out of school due in part to their housing costs. Do not make this mistake. If staying at home is at all an option for you, *do it*! But remember to always be grateful. Help take care of the house and yard because your family is effectively helping you graduate earlier.

Roommates: If living with family is not an option, or if you already live on your own, then one of the best ways to decrease your housing expense is by getting a roommate or roommates. A roommate will quickly transform an unused bedroom into $300 to $600 per month of savings. That could cut your rent or mortgage down by half! But be careful: not any roommate will do. Before you allow just anyone to live with you, make sure they will mesh well with you and your schedule. A background check and interview are always a good idea. The website www.zillow.com offers a great property management interface that includes background and credit checks for prospective tenants.

The right roommate could not only save you money, but they may also even help you get through school. Talk to your classmates—chances are good that some of them are currently looking for a new place or will be soon. It would be ideal if you could live with a fellow classmate who is going through the same program as you. And why stop at one? All of your empty bedrooms should be making you money. The more the merrier!

House-hack: House-hacking is a simple way to own property without paying for most or all of it. I will demonstrate with a simple example. You buy a triplex close to your school for $250,000. With a 3 percent down payment, your monthly mortgage should be around $1,400 per month. You then live in one unit and rent out the other two for $800 per month per unit. Not only is the incoming rent covering your mortgage payment and building equity in your investment, but you're making an additional $200 per month profit. This is the technique I used while in school, and it worked wonderfully. I bought a single-family three-bedroom home close to my school. I took one bedroom and rented out the other two for $500 per room. This covered 75 percent of my mortgage payment! With my decreased housing cost, I was able to work part-time and attend school full-time. House-hacking is an outstanding way to own property without sacrificing school. I highly recommend this technique if you're looking to buy or already own a home.

Transportation

Behind housing, transportation is the average American's second largest expense. Between car payments, insurance, gas, maintenance, and bus or train fares, transportation costs can add up big time. If you can decrease your need for transportation, you will not only save the money associated with it, but you will save the time spent commuting. Below I have listed the five best ways to either eliminate or decrease your transportation costs.

Live Close to School and Work: One of the best ways to cut down on transportation costs is to decrease the distance between where you live and the places you need to be, especially work and school. A good example of this would be living in the dormitories on your school's campus. Obviously, there are costs associated with moving closer to either work or school. However, if you are commuting two hours a day, five days a week, just to save a few hundred bucks a month in rent, then you may want to rethink your plan. Wasting that much time every week can have a huge impact on your productivity in school. If you can move closer to school and/or work without significantly increasing your housing expenses, you should probably go for it.

Online Courses: Chances are good that your school offers some of your courses online. Especially if you're in the first two years of your degree. I recommend taking advantage of these courses whenever possible, especially if your commute to school is significant. Every course you take online eliminates the additional transportation cost associated with taking it on campus.

Used Vehicles: Automobiles are perhaps the world's worst investment. In fact, they are not an investment at all. They are a liability. Between gasoline, insurance, maintenance, and depreciation, you're pretty much guaranteed to consistently lose money. The best way to mitigate this is to not buy a car in the first place—*cough cough*, bicycle, *cough cough*. However, if you must have a vehicle, *do not* buy a new one. Many young adults are lured in by the luxury and perceived prestige of a brand-new vehicle, only to be enslaved by a five to seven year car payment that is usually much higher than they can afford. Don't fall into this trap. Shop around for quality used vehicles instead. Something that will safely get you from point A to point B without all of the unnecessary extras. A bigger car payment equals more time spent at work, which equals less time spent on your studies.

PRO TIP: Shop for car insurance annually. Auto insurance is a significant monthly expense that you can usually decrease with a few phone calls. Prices fluctuate yearly between companies, and new companies pop up all the time. What you thought was a good price last year may not be this year. Always shop around for insurance on an annual basis. This could save you quite a bit of cash. I've done this for the last two years, and it has saved me $40 per month each year. That equates to $1,440 saved over two years!

Bicycles: Maybe it's the mechanical engineer in me, but the bicycle is hands down my favorite human creation. It is by far the most efficient form of travel and should be taken advantage of whenever possible. Not only are bicycles much less expensive than automobiles but they will also provide you with valuable exercise and stress relief, not to mention the decrease in carbon emissions. If you live relatively close to campus, a bicycle should be your form of transportation. By the time you figure in stoplights, parking, and walking time, driving to school is often slower than cycling. With a bicycle, there is no traffic, no waiting for parking spots; and, most times, you can ride all the way to your classroom door. Additionally, most campuses are becoming more sustainable, which means fewer parking spaces and more bike lanes. Your wallet, your health, and the planet will thank you. Ride a bike!

Travel Efficiently: An engineer's favorite three words are efficiency, efficiency, and efficiency! We love getting more output per unit input. You should apply this mind-set to your daily travel. Try to think ahead and combine your trips whenever possible. If you're already out and about, think about future trips you can eliminate quickly by picking up what you need while you're already out. Carpool whenever possible and use public transportation when it makes sense. Get creative with it. Chances are good that there are several ways you can increase your travel efficiency. You just need to find them!

Education

In 2019 the average cost of tuition for an in-state public school was $9,212 per year and $31,875 per year for private colleges. This huge cost can be quite burdensome for any student, especially if they plan to pay for school out of pocket. Unfortunately, these costs are going up an average of 3 percent every year with no end in sight.[11] The good news is that there are several things you can do to decrease or eliminate these high costs. Below are the five best ways to do just that.

Scholarships and Grants: Free money. Let me say that again. *Free Money!* When you're figuring out how to pay for school, the very first step you should take is applying for all the scholarships and grants you can find. This is money set aside by the government and other private donors meant to assist students who need it. Don't think that you need straight As to get a scholarship. There are many full and partial scholarships given out to regular students all the time, especially if you are

---

[11] NCES National Center for Education Statistics. "Table 330.10. Average Undergraduate Tuition and Fees and Room and Board Rates Charged for Full-Time Students in Degree-Granting Postsecondary Institutions, by Level and Control of Institution: Selected Years, 1963–64 through 2018–19." https://nces.ed.gov/programs/digest/d19/tables/dt19_330.10.asp?current=yes

a minority or a veteran. Check with your school's financial aid office and apply for as many as you can.

In addition to scholarships, the US government offers grant money through their Free Application for Student Aid (FAFSA) program. Go to www.fafsa.ed.gov and fill out the application to see if you qualify for any grant money. Keep in mind that this application is for both grants and student loans, which brings me to the next point.

Student Loans: I understand that student loans are a sensitive topic, and many of you would probably rather eat dirt than be subjected to another monthly payment. In most cases, I would completely agree with this mind-set. However, you shouldn't let your fear of debt get in the way of rational thought. This fear of debt causes many students to work longer hours during the week, which usually either limits their course load or leads to poor performance in school. Both of these outcomes generally result in a delayed graduation.

Now you may be saying, "Yes, but at least they saved all that interest money!" You are correct. But I'm here to tell you that they still lost a ton of money—potentially even *more* money than they saved in interest. Let me demonstrate with an example. Let's assume that you completely financed your education using a $50,000 student loan at 6 percent interest. After a standard ten-year repayment plan at $555 per month, you will end up paying $66,612 of principal and interest to the bank. This ends up being $16,612 paid in just interest, which is quite substantial and should not be taken lightly.

Now for the flip side. Let's assume that you bypassed the need for student loans by working full-time throughout school so that you could graduate with absolutely zero debt. However, because of your work schedule, you weren't able to take a full load of courses every semester. So you end up graduating just one semester later than planned. No big deal, right? After all, it's just one semester. At least you saved all the interest money, right? Not so fast. By graduating later than planned, you are effectively postponing your engineering salary. In 2020, the average starting salary for an entry-level engineer was $72,614. If we assume that you delay your graduation by just one semester (four months = 0.33 years), then you are essentially losing $23,962 of potential salary (0.33 years x $72,614 per year = $23,962). Assuming a 22 percent income tax rate we come to **$18,690** in lost net income ($23,962 x (1-0.22) = $18,690**).** In summary, by graduating debt-free, you saved $16,612 in interest payments while at the same time losing $18,690 in delayed salary. Now if you subtract the two values, it shows that, by *not t*aking out loans, you actually *lost* **$2,078**. And this loss will only increase the longer graduation is pushed out.

I present this example to hopefully clear up some of the misplaced fear you may have toward student debt. While many people are quick to point out the significant savings when graduating debt-free, they fail to point out the losses due to a potential deferred salary. Everyone's situation is a little different, but I highly suggest doing the calculations yourself before you close the door on student loans because they may actually save you money in the long run.

Community College: Universities are expensive. As previously mentioned, the average cost per year for a public in-state university is $9,212 and even higher for out-of-state and private schools. A great way to delay paying these high tuition rates is to take advantage of your local community college. In 2019, the average yearly cost of a two-year community college was only $3,213. That's almost a third the price of an in-state university! Most community colleges will offer most, if not all, of the courses you will need in your first two years and maybe even beyond. Take advantage of your local community college if you can. It could end up saving you thousands of dollars!

Tuition Assistance Programs: The first time I heard about an employer paying for its employees' tuition, I couldn't believe it. It seemed too good to be true. But in reality, it is actually quite common. Starbucks, UPS, Chevron, Raytheon, Intel, and Apple are just a few companies that offer tuition assistance to their employees. A tuition assistance program is essentially an employer's way of investing in its employees with the hope of the employee becoming more educated and productive in the workplace. Typically, the employer will pay for most or all of the employee's tuition costs as long as a specific GPA is met.

Additionally, many companies require that the employee stay employed after graduation for two years or so. This is essentially the employer guaranteeing a return on their investment. I was lucky enough to get a job at a company with a tuition assistance program during my junior year. It saved me roughly $30,000 in tuition, and it was wonderful! If you have to work while you're in school, I highly recommend looking for a company that has a tuition assistance program.

Textbooks: The college textbook industry is one of the most infuriating things I can think of. They take advantage of students year after year with "new" editions that hardly change from the year before. Yet they still charge hundreds of dollars per book. But until something is done to regulate this blatant price gouging, students will just have to make do. Below is a list of some good ways to mitigate the high cost of textbooks.

⇒ **Buy Used Books:** Generally, used textbooks are much cheaper than new textbooks.

⇒ **Buy the E-book Version:** E-books are always cheaper than a hard copy

⇒ **Buy Online:** You can almost always find textbooks cheaper online, especially if you can find an international version.

⇒ **Borrow from Upperclassmen:** Most upperclassmen will have many of the textbooks you need just collecting dust on their shelves. You should make friends with upperclassmen and ask if you can borrow or rent their textbooks for a semester. Also, remember to pay it forward when other students ask to borrow your textbooks.

⇒ **Rent Your Textbooks:** Renting textbooks is always cheaper than buying.

General Frugal Living

Housing, transportation, and education are likely your three largest expenses. If you can eliminate or decrease any or all of them, you will most definitely be saving yourself a lot of money. But besides those big three, there are several other areas that offer potential savings. Below I have listed a few more tips for general frugal living.

Create Your Budget: The first step to frugal living is to know where your money is actually going. There are several useful apps that can help with viewing and maintaining a budget. I personally use an app called Mint for my budgeting. Most banks offer a budgeting feature directly through their mobile apps. Many of these apps will link directly to all of your checking, savings, and credit card accounts to give you a live picture of your personal expenses.

Once you have a good handle on where your money is going every month, you can begin to analyze each purchase or payment to determine if it was completely necessary or if it can be decreased. For instance, I recently saved $120 per month by canceling my cable subscription. All of the television I want can be found through streaming services or somewhere else online, so paying for cable was a total waste of money. Hopefully, once you have a good handle on your monthly expenses, you will uncover similar opportunities for savings.

Credit Card Cash Back: Credit cards are a touchy topic. Most people will tell you to avoid them at all costs because their interest rates are just too high, which is true. But if you never carry over a monthly balance, the interest will never hurt you. I understand that it is a big *if* for most people. Fully paying off your credit cards every month requires strict discipline and control over your spending habits. But if you are someone who has this level of control, credit cards can offer a nice incentive—cash back baby! Cash back is essentially free money that will accumulate based on the money you've spent, usually 1 percent to 2 percent. If you use a credit card for everything, you are essentially getting a 1 percent to 2 percent discount on everything you buy. This can really add up at the end of every month. Keep in mind that the majority of people do not pay off their credit cards every month. If they did, credit card companies would not offer this much cash back. Before you start using credit cards to this degree, you should make sure that you have tight control over your expenses and spending habits.

Shop Around: Whenever you're making a significant purchase, you should make sure you're getting the best price. Always check other vendors for a lower price. At the very least, check the price on Amazon before you buy anything significant. Most stores will price match if the item is sold by Amazon. The main point here is patience. Always exercise patience before buying anything significant. Take time to verify that the item or service is essential and that you are getting the very best price possible.

- -

PRO TIP: www.camelcamelcamel.com. Speaking of Amazon, there is a great website called camelcamelcamel.com that will show you the entire price history of an item on Amazon. Just copy the URL from Amazon and paste it into the camelcamelcamel.com search bar. You will quickly see if the current price is high or low historically. Additionally, if you're willing to wait, camelcamelcamel.com will notify you when your desired item's price drops.

- -

Student Discounts: Student discounts are everywhere. Never ever leave home without your student ID card. Amazon, Apple, AT&T, and Costco are just a few companies that offer discounts to their student customers. To list every company that offers student discounts would take most of this book. Just make a habit of asking anyone and everyone if they offer student discounts before you buy anything, especially at businesses that are close to your school. You'll be surprised at the savings.

Buy Used and Refurbished Stuff: One of the easiest ways to save money is to avoid buying new stuff. Especially big-ticket items like vehicles, furniture, and electronics. These categories demand huge premiums whenever they are purchased brand new. And then lose a significant amount of their value the moment they are unpackaged. Fortunately, you can often find perfectly acceptable alternatives that are gently used or refurbished. A quick search on Craigslist will provide thousands of quality used items. And Amazon almost always has quality refurbished options when searching for electronics. You can also do it the old-fashioned way and check out your local yard sales and thrift shops. Either way, you'll end up with some pretty cool stuff and save a nice chunk of change.

Making Work...Work

Even after your cost of living is decreased, it still may be difficult to decrease the time spent at work. Your job may require a minimum number of hours per week for employment. If this is the case, you should speak with your supervisor to determine if there is any way you can change your schedule to be more accommodating to school. Many times, employers will be cooperative and work something out that benefits both you and the company. However, sometimes this is not the case. Your supervisor may deny your request and demand that you continue working on an inconvenient schedule. This is your cue to start looking for alternatives. Remember, your first priority is school, not work. Your job should accommodate your education, not the other way around. Below I have listed the best ways to make money while not sacrificing your education.

Freelancing: Are you good at something? Do other people want to be good at that same thing? If so, then those people will most likely be willing to pay you for it. Freelancing is one of the best ways to make great money on a flexible schedule. Some examples include sports, musical instruments, math, coding, and writing. You'd be surprised how much people are willing to pay for private instruction. While in school, I made about $300 a week working only six hours teaching private swimming lessons. It worked out great because I was able to schedule the lessons around my classes and still make enough money to cover my expenses. Take inventory of your own skills and abilities; you may be able to use one for your own freelancing business.

Work on Your Own Time: Not all jobs require a strict forty-hour Monday through Friday schedule. Thanks to the internet and mobile technology, there are now several employment opportunities that offer extreme flexibility. For example, as an Uber or Lyft driver, you can literally work as much or as little as you want and at whatever times are convenient for you. Other great options include delivering for Amazon Flex, DoorDash, Grubhub, or Postmates, all of which offer extremely flexible schedules and reasonable pay. Keep in mind that these are just a few examples of many. Do not make the mistake of thinking that you have to work nine to five Monday through Friday to have a job. There are several flexible part-time options available. It is just a matter of finding one that works for you.

Work-Study Programs: The Federal Work-Study Program serves as a great opportunity to work part-time while not sacrificing school. The program's primary purpose is to assist students who are in financial need by providing them with flexible employment, which is often related to the student's field of study. To qualify for this program, you must fill out the Federal Application for Student Aid (FAFSA), then coordinate with your school's financial aid office to apply for any work-study positions available.

It may feel like we've strayed from the topic of school. But remember, in order to give yourself the best chance of success, you'll need to dedicate big quality chunks of time every day to your studies. Your schooling must become your no-questions-asked number-one priority with the rest of your obligations becoming flexible around it. The past several pages were dedicated to helping you create that reality for yourself. The less money you need and the more flexible of a schedule you can create for yourself, the more time you can spend studying. Don't forget that I am writing about this stuff because it is what *actually* causes students to struggle. All of this knowledge is based on my own and others' actual experiences.

Your schooling must become your no-questions-asked number one priority with the rest of your obligations becoming flexible around it.

The Black Hole of Social Media

The average American spends about two hours per day on social media.[12] This includes YouTube, Facebook, Instagram, Twitter, Reddit, TikTok, Snapchat, and everything else in between. Two hours per day! That equates to five years over a lifetime! Isn't that absolutely insane? Think about the valuable things that could be done with two extra hours every day. You could exercise, spend quality time with loved ones, read

------

[12] "Daily Time Spent on Social Networking by Internet Users Worldwide from 2012 to 2019." https://www.statista.com/statistics/433871/daily-social-media-usage-worldwide/.

a book, be creative, play with your dog, or *study*! Ding, ding, ding! That is an extra fourteen hours per week right there. A whole extra day you can dedicate to school just by killing your social media addiction. Now some of you are probably saying, "Ugh…are you crazy?" To those of you, I would ask, "Do you even remember what you scrolled through on your socials earlier today or yesterday? Is it ever that memorable of an experience? Why would you spend so much time on something every day that is so unimpactful?"

Let's go through a quick scenario. You sit down at your desk with plans to do some homework. But right as you open your textbook, your phone goes off with a notification from Instagram, a comment from a friend on a photo. You check the comment and respond. Then instead of putting your phone away, you scroll your feed for fifteen minutes and then do the same on Facebook and Snapchat. Suddenly it's two hours later, and you're watching a video of a cat doing handstands on YouTube. You've been sucked into the black hole of social media before you even knew what happened. Does this scenario sound familiar? The ability of social media to draw and hold our attention is astounding. Usually, we save the word "addicted" for things like drugs and gambling. But when was the last day that you didn't check your social media? Do you ever find yourself on Facebook or Instagram before you even realize how you got there, even though you just checked it only ten minutes ago? If that is not an addiction, then I don't know what is. These companies know how your brain works and are exploiting it to no end. All in an effort to grab and hold your attention for as long and as frequently as possible. This completely kills productivity and creativity. Whenever we have a spare second, we are instantly on our phones frantically checking in on whatever app is screaming the loudest. This behavior is not healthy. Remember your priorities, people!

These realizations are why I eventually deleted my social media accounts. I would find myself mindlessly scrolling Facebook before I even remembered pulling out my phone. This zombielike behavior eventually made me feel, well, crappy. It made me feel like I was turning my back on my potential by wasting so much time on my phone. Eventually, I started to ask myself, "Does this add any true value to my day?" The answer was always "no!" So I deleted Facebook, simple as that. It was hard in the beginning. It seriously felt like withdrawing from a drug. But after a month or so, I didn't even miss it. It's been almost five years now, and I couldn't be happier with my decision. I feel like I removed some invisible leech that was slowly sucking away all of my creativity and ambition. Now I feel normal again. I feel like Neo when he woke up from the matrix—except a lot less gooey.

My experience was in line with a recent study that was done at the University of Pennsylvania[13], which shows a link between social media usage and increased levels of depression and loneliness. This finding is not surprising. I sincerely recommend that you take a good hard look at the amount of time you spend on social media. Because if you're anything like the average American, there is a lot of time and happiness to be gained by killing the addiction. Also, remember that you are on a path that is *not* average. By pursuing an engineering degree, you are setting yourself apart as someone that does not shy away from a challenge. While others are wasting their lives away in the never-ending scroll, you will be spending your time on something that is actually meaningful. On something that *will* have a real impact on your life.

---

[13] Hunt, Melissa G., Rachel Marx, Courtney Lipson, and Jordyn Young. "No More FOMO: Limiting Social Media Decreases Loneliness and Depression." *Journal of Social and Clinical Psychology* 37, no. 10 (2018): 751–768.

Quick Recap

In addition to the monetary cost of school, time will also be a big part of the payment for your degree. And unlike the dollar price tag, the payment of time can be tricky. It is variable from person to person and from week to week. But one thing is for sure. You will need *a lot* of it. And in order to get it, you *must* make your studies your first priority. Engineering school is already difficult enough. But it will become nearly impossible if it is not your highest priority. Almost everything else in your life needs to become flexible to accommodate your education—not the other way around.

You will need large chunks of dedicated study time every day. This begins by getting a good handle on where you currently spend your time. If you spend a lot of time at work each week, the best way to decrease that need is to decrease your cost of living. Analyze your housing, transportation, education, and other expenses for opportunities to save money, therefore decreasing the need to work. If your current job won't allow a decrease in hours, you should consider a form of work that does. And lastly, take a good hard look at the time you spend on social media because you will not have two hours a day to waste. It may be a good idea to either delete or take a break from your socials. Again, it is important to note that I speak from experience. I went into engineering school not realizing how much time it would require, and I paid the price. Do not make the same mistake that I and so many others did. Free up as much time as you can *beforehand*. Trust me, your education will demand it.

SIX

SUSTAINABILITY AND EFFICIENCY

People of accomplishment rarely sit back and let things happen to them. They go out and happen to things.
—Leonardo Da Vinci

Become the Tortoise

Do you remember that old story about the tortoise and the hare? In the end, why do you think the tortoise beat the hare? It sure wasn't due to its raw speed or quick reflexes. No, the tortoise was victorious because it was efficient and resilient. It avoided overexertion by finding a speed that was sustainable, then slowly but surely crossed the finish line. It wasn't flashy or fast, but it got the job done. The tortoise knew its own limits and planned accordingly. It didn't let its eagerness to finish quickly get in the way of rationality. This is the strategy that is going to get you through engineering school. Too many students burn out from self-induced stress caused by unrealistic expectations. They overload themselves with the intention of moving up their graduation date but actually end up postponing it. A sustainable schedule and efficient lifestyle are vital ingredients to your success. The potential costs of trying to go too fast are not worth it. A gradual and methodical mind-set will keep you in this race. This chapter will show you how to implement these ideas into your own schedule and lifestyle.

Sustainability

I used to work at a gym, and January was by far our busiest time of the year. All the New Year's resolutioners would come flocking in with visions of six-packs and tight butts. They would all start with the same determined look in their eyes. "It's only kale and a treadmill from here on out!" Bless their little hearts. Most would do pretty well in the beginning. Then within two weeks, the new demanding exercise schedule and strict diet would begin to take its toll. They would miss a few workouts, then maybe sneak a couple of fast-food meals. I think you know where this is going. Eventually, February would roll around, and the gym would go back to normal. Almost everyone who started in January would revert to their normal routines with goals left unaccomplished.

So what happened? Why do so many people fail when attempting to get into shape? You guessed it: no thought is given to sustainability. Everyone wants their dream body as fast as possible, so they put themselves on the most extreme regimen imaginable and just assume that it's sustainable. The problem is most people cannot make such an extreme change and stick to it. Can you think of a similar experience in your own life? One where you've had a big goal that you wanted to achieve so badly it hurt? So blinded by your own ambition, you bite off way more than you can chew and gun it to 1,000 mph. Then the work turns out to be way harder and less fun than you imagined, and before you know it, your motivation gets dethroned by frustration and exhaustion—all because you had unrealistic expectations and went too hard, too fast. The result? Your big goal remains just a goal and you are left feeling like a piece of crap. Does this sound familiar?

I have watched many of my personal friends fall into the trap of neglecting sustainability with their schooling. And I can tell you, it never ends well. Most end up failing one or two of their courses, or they barely pass everything with Cs and destroy their GPA along the way. By the end of the semester, most end up feeling exhausted and mentally destroyed. Some even changed majors because they couldn't handle the mental toll of their underperformance. Their impatience got the best of them, and they paid the price. All I ask is that you learn everything you can from other people's mistakes. Sustainability is key. I want to help you avoid those unfortunate outcomes by helping you create a sustainable lifestyle and schedule.

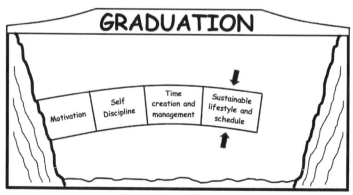

The Bridge of Graduation

Always learn everything you can from other people's mistakes.

Sustainable Mind-Set

The major difference between people who accomplish great things and people who stay at home on the couch is not IQ or raw talent. It's their mind-set. People of great accomplishment have proper expectations, adapt quickly to failure, and always maintain optimism. They don't waste time with excuses or negativity. Their energy is spent figuring out how to succeed and act toward their goals. They know the awesome power of mind-set and exploit it to their advantage. Every experience you have is filtered through your mind. It has the power to make a mountain out of a molehill or a molehill out of a mountain. That is why your mind-set is so massively important, and it all begins with expectations.

Realistic Expectations

The quickest route to disappointment is to expect an outcome that isn't going to happen. For example, as a freshman, I truly believed that I could pass my classes with the same level of effort I gave in high school. Talk about disappointment! As you can imagine, it didn't take long for those expectations to be obliterated. They were totally unrealistic and resulted in several failed courses and a severely damaged ego. I want to save you from this disappointment. Because students can only take so much failure before it starts to take a heavy toll. That is why it is crucial that you enter engineering school with realistic expectations. Let's explore three of the most common disparities between incoming students' expectations and the reality of engineering school.

You Will Not Love All of Your Classes: When I was doing the research for this book, one of the most consistent complaints I came across was how surprised students were to find out that they did not enjoy their classes as much as they imagined they would. Don't make the mistake of expecting engineering school to be some whimsical experience full of magical science and 100 percent enjoyment. This is not Hogwarts. This is real life, so get that idea out of your head now. While many of your classes will be extremely interesting and enjoyable, you must come to terms with the fact that some of them will be rather unenjoyable. Just expect it.

Many of your courses are required to support the knowledge you will gain later in your degree, so they should be viewed as building blocks toward a higher cause. You may not like them in the moment, but the skills learned are essential. You must build this foundation before you can take the more interesting courses later in your degree. Just be patient and expect that you will not enjoy every course on your schedule. But know that all of your classes together will mold you into the engineer you want to be. Think of them as your childhood vegetables. Did you like eating your broccoli as a child? Probably not, but it was for your own good.

School Will Probably Be More Difficult Than You Imagined:
We have already touched on this in chapter 3, but it's worth restating. Engineering school will be difficult. Probably more difficult than you have prepared for. Too many students are blindsided by the gap between their expectations and reality. Do yourself a favor and reevaluate your preparations. Overpreparation never caused anyone to fail. But underpreparation causes failure all the time. Overprepare and adjust

your efforts as needed. Don't allow yourself to be blindsided by the workload.

Don't Look Too Far Ahead: We live in a world of instant gratification—one where we've all been conditioned to expect quick results everywhere—Fast food, same-day delivery, and on-demand entertainment. You will soon be able to order something from your toilet seat and have it delivered by a drone minutes later. Talk about convenience! I hate to break it to you, but engineering school doesn't work like that. Your degree will not be a quick endeavor. Your progress will feel slow at times, so it is best to keep your focus on the courses and material right in front of you.

As a freshman and sophomore, it can be particularly easy to get discouraged by dwelling on how many courses you have left to graduate. Especially when it feels like you've already run several marathons back to back just to get where you are now. In these moments, ask yourself the following question. "Will stressing about how many classes I have left help me pass my next exam?" Nope, no way, never. In fact, it will only hinder your ability to focus and drain your motivation. It's best to just keep your head down and tackle what is right in front of you. Before you know it, you will have made some real progress. Again, how do you eat an elephant? One bite at a time.

Stress Management

Stress and engineering school go together like flies on poop. They are an inseparable pair. In many ways, your graduation will depend more on how well you manage stress than it will on how smart you are. Again, it all comes down to sustainability. Think of yourself as a ship on a trans-Atlantic voyage that is continuously taking on water. The ship's survival completely depends on how fast the crew can remove the incoming water. If they do not manage the incoming water successfully, or if the leak gets too big, the ship will sink and never arrive at its destination. As your stress level increases, you must maintain sustainability. If you don't, you will sink like a ship full of water.

Obviously, the first step in stress management is to not overload yourself in the first place. The next step is managing your remaining stress successfully. Below are some of the best research-backed ways to mitigate and manage stress, most of which I personally used with great success during my schooling and still use to this day.

- -

In many ways, your graduation will depend more on how well you manage stress than it will on how smart you are.

- -

Prioritize Your Day: Being able to quickly prioritize your to-do list on a daily basis will become one of the most important skills you develop as a student. By doing so, you can easily eliminate large amounts of potential stress every day. Establish your to-do list, and ask yourself this simple question: "If I could magically have one item on my list complete, which one would it be?" The answer is almost always the item that has the most stress associated with not completing it. It is now your number one priority for the day. After it is complete, repeat this exercise for the remaining items on your list. By prioritizing in this manner, you are effectively minimizing your stress every day.

Establish and Follow a Plan: One of the best ways to limit future stress is to establish and follow a well-thought-out plan. For instance, let's say you have three homework assignments due in one week. A good low-stress plan would be to get one assignment done every two days. This way, you should be able to perform quality work without the stress of an immediate deadline. Now let's look at the flip side. Let's say you neglect your homework in order to go on a weekend camping trip. The trip may be fun. But you have just introduced stress that didn't exist before. Stress that comes with having to finish all three homework assignments in a much shorter time frame. In addition to the stress that may come with lower performance due to inadequate time spent on each assignment.

When it comes to executing a good plan, it really comes down to a simple comparison—your future stress levels if you execute the plan compared to your future stress levels if you don't execute the plan. It's that simple. For instance, compare how disappointed you would be if you missed that weekend camping trip to how stressed you would be if you were only able to finish half of your homework. Put yourself in your future self's shoes. I often use this comparison whenever I am faced with a potential deviation from my own plans. It is very effective in revealing the potential outcome of your decisions. Remember, plans are only good as your discipline to follow them.

Establish Your True North: A good place to start when trying to manage your own stress is establishing a "true north." In other words, give yourself a singular direction, and therefore a singular purpose. In this case, your singular purpose will be graduation. Having a singular purpose can really remove a lot of the waste and ambiguity in your day-to-day life, which in turn removes a ton of unnecessary stress. It creates the "true north filter," if you will, through which you can run all potential thoughts, feelings, decisions, and actions to determine if they are beneficial or detrimental to your singular purpose. It's continually asking yourself, "Does this thought, feeling, decision, or action get me closer to graduation?" If the answer is no, then the thought, feeling, decision, or action stops right there. Don't let it get past the filter. If the answer is yes, then it is allowed past the filter and into reality.

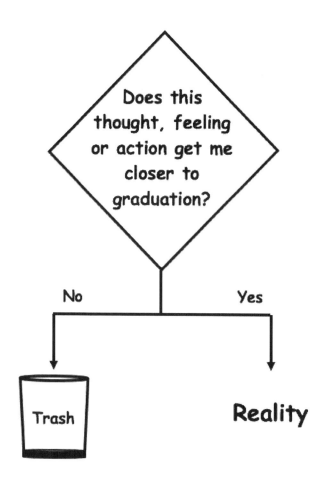

Become an Optimist: If you look for the light, you can often find it. But if you look for darkness, it will be all you ever see. —Iroh, *Avatar: The Last Airbender*. I love that quote because it perfectly illustrates how, like a virus, negativity can completely take over your mind, create crippling stress, and inhibit your ability to get things done. I'm sure you know someone who has this negativity virus. Someone who complains about everything, compliments nobody, insults everyone behind their backs, and blames anyone but themselves. Do you ever feel particularly motivated or inspired after being with that person? I didn't think so. Common symptoms of the negativity virus are thoughts like, "I've already failed one exam; why should I try anymore?" and "I study twice as long as my friends, but they all get better grades than me. I must not have what it takes." Negative thoughts like these can completely kill your productivity and will lead you in the opposite direction of your true north.

This is where the optimism comes in. As an optimist, you will recognize that those negative and stress-causing thoughts actually pull you away from your goals and therefore have no place in your life. They are a complete and utter waste of your time and energy. The only thoughts, actions, and behaviors that you will invest in are the ones that will help you succeed. For example, if you fail an exam, you will not dwell on your disappointment. You will instead focus on how you will improve your strategy for the next exam. And if your peers perform better than you, then you will not resent them. Instead, you will be happy for their success and try to learn what you can from their approach. Recognizing and focusing on the positive and productive aspects of every situation will remove more unnecessary stress than almost any other activity. An optimistic attitude helps you to focus only on things that you can control, learn from your mistakes without dwelling on them, and never lose belief in your own abilities.

Recognizing and focusing on the positive and productive aspects of every situation will remove more unnecessary stress than almost any other activity.

Maintain Proper Perspective: Are you particularly disappointed when you don't shoot a hole in one on a par four? No, you are not. That is because when golfing, you have a proper perspective in the situation. You understand that a hole in one is not probable, so you don't invest very much emotion into not shooting one. Many students enter engineering school expecting a hole in one. They were straight A students in high school, so they expect more of the same in college, then promptly lose their minds when they earn their first B+. I've spoken with college advisers and heard stories of students changing majors because they literally could not mentally handle getting Bs and Cs. Crazy, right? This could have been avoided if they had a proper perspective. I am not saying that you should expect to get low grades. All I am saying is that you must approach engineering school with an understanding and expectation of its difficulty. Then your motivation and ego will remain intact, if and when you face a setback.

Live in the Present: We suffer more in our imagination than in reality. —Seneca. You'd be surprised how much of your own stress is created by dwelling on something that already happened or worrying about a potential future outcome. Why would you waste time and energy focusing on stuff that has already happened or hasn't happened? You cannot change the past, and worrying about a future outcome isn't going to help you prepare for it. The present is where all things get done. It is the only place that is under your control, so that is where you must mentally and physically exist. Learn from your past mistakes and implement what you've learned into your present actions to shape your future.

We suffer more in our imagination than in reality. —Seneca

Learn to Say No: Being selfish is usually viewed as a negative characteristic. However, while you are in engineering school, being selfish may actually be a good thing. Your time and energy will be largely spoken for by your studies. The last thing you should be doing is making other non-value-added commitments. Let someone else help your friend move. Let someone else take on that extra project at work. And let someone else host your buddy's birthday party. Learn to say *no* and feel good about it. If your friends, family, and coworkers knew the amount of stress it would cause you to lose the time they were asking for, they would most likely not ask for it in the first place. So don't feel bad about saying no. There are times in your life when it's okay to be selfish. This is one of them.

Sleep: Your ability to handle stress on a daily basis is directly proportional to the amount of sleep you are getting each night. Without regular sleep every night, you become a less capable version of yourself. Your ability to process and deal with stressful situations decreases. If stress is a rainstorm, then a good night's sleep is the protective roof over your head. It gives you the energy and mental clarity to navigate and overcome your daily stressors. We will go into the importance of sleep more in the next chapter. But for now, don't make that mistake of sacrificing sleep on a regular basis. Very few things will burn you more quickly.

Diet: While we are on the subject of keeping your body at its highest level of performance, it would be irresponsible if we didn't touch on the importance of diet. High-quality performance requires high-quality fuel. You wouldn't expect a rocket ship to take off on regular unleaded. So why would you expect to perform at a high level fueled by doughnuts and a soda. I could write an entire chapter on this subject, but I promised myself I would keep this book relatively short, so let's just hit the most important points.

⇒ **Raw and Simple Ingredients:** One of the best ways to manage and improve your diet is to incorporate more raw and simple ingredients: fruits, veggies, nuts, lean meats, and so forth. If a food's ingredient list is super long and you can't pronounce most of the items, then chances are good that the food is not very nutritious. A nice trick when shopping is to stick to the outside perimeter of the grocery store. Typically, this is where you'll find the most whole and nutritious foods. The artificial and highly processed foods are usually kept in the aisles, so stay away!

⇒ **Meal Prep:** Want to eat healthy while also saving time and money? Meal prep is your answer. Preparing a week's meals in advance allows you to control your entire week's diet with one decision instead of several. A couple of hours of cooking on a Sunday afternoon can save you from all those $8 fast food mistakes throughout the week—not to mention all the money you'll save.

⇒ **Affordability:** Despite what you may believe, it does not have to be expensive to eat healthily. People think that in order to eat healthily, you have to shop at Whole Foods or Trader Joe's. This is not true! There are several ways to eat well without breaking the bank. Buying in bulk at stores like Costco or Sam's Club can save hundreds of dollars throughout the year. Additionally, most grocery stores include bulk food bin sections nowadays where you can fill a bag with as much rice, grain, flour, oats, lentils, dried fruits, or beans as you like. This method saves quite a bit of processing and packaging, which in turn saves you money. Another good option is online shopping. I have recently turned to Amazon for many of my bulk and non-perishable foods like rice and canned goods. These are just a few options of many. Get creative!

⇒ **Carry Snacks:** You will be spending quite a bit of time at school each day, so it's important to think ahead and always have some high-quality snacks on hand. Granola bars, dried fruit, nuts, seeds, and hard-boiled eggs are all great options. Having good snacks on hand can save you from a late-night trip to Sugartown.

⇒ **Carry Water:** Hopefully, I don't need to sell you on the benefits of drinking plenty of water. It is required for life, so drink it—a lot. To be more precise, we should all be drinking at least two liters per day. So do yourself a favor and invest in a good water bottle that you can easily carry wherever you go. This will save you from the soda machine and ensure that you remain properly hydrated.

⇒ **Coffee:** If you are like most of the people on this planet, you consume caffeine on a daily basis. As you progress through school, your consumption of caffeine will most likely increase, especially during exam weeks. With the advent of the energy drink, I'd like to share a few words advocating for good old-fashioned coffee. Not only will you save money by choosing coffee over energy drinks, but it actually has health benefits associated with it. Coffee has been shown to help prevent type 2 diabetes, Parkinson's, and liver disease. Energy drinks are full of sugar and other chemicals that do more harm than good. If you need a quick pick-me-up, reach for a hot cup of joe and leave the energy drinks alone.

Meditation: For thousands of years, monks, religious figures, scholars, and other influencers have been using meditation as a way to clear the mind, relieve stress, and gain perspective. Usually, when a technique sticks around for that long, it's because it works. I can personally attest to its effectiveness. I have consistently experienced noticeable stress relief from short five to fifteen-minute meditation sessions. Although the topic of meditation may be a bit obscure to you at first, a quick search on Google, YouTube, or the app store will yield dozens of "meditation for beginners" options. I personally use an app called Headspace. It does cost around $80 per year, but it is very well put together, and I highly recommend it as a good place to start.

Mental Health Therapy: Many people think that you need to be diagnosed with something in order to benefit from therapy. Well, get that idea out of your head right now. Anyone and everyone can benefit from therapy. I have plenty of mentally healthy and very successful friends who see a therapist on a regular basis. There are huge benefits to just being able to off-load your thoughts, concerns, and stressors on to someone else. It doesn't even have to be a licensed therapist. It can be anyone who you trust to listen to and support you on a regular basis. Additionally, your school should have counselors ready and waiting to help you through any issue, so take advantage of it. Just don't make the mistake of thinking you can bottle everything up without consequence. Talk to someone. Other people's perspectives and experiences can serve as some of the best stress relief.

Exercise: You know that magic cure-all pill that everyone is looking for? The one that can cure diseases, increase happiness, burn fat, increase intelligence, and give you energy? Well, I'm sorry to report that it doesn't exist. However, there is something that is very close. And it's free! You guessed it; the answer is exercise—regular exercise to be more precise. Research continues to prove that regular daily exercise is the single most beneficial activity we can engage in. Not only does it burn calories, but it also relieves stress and anxiety, increases happiness, prevents disease, increases energy, increases mental performance, and can literally help you live longer.[14] Why would you not take advantage of these benefits? If I could only recommend one thing for stress relief, it would be regular exercise. The numerous benefits are too substantial to ignore. Which is why we will dive more into the incredible power of exercise in chapter 8.

PRO TIP: Ride a bike to school. With just one activity, you can save money, save time, help the environment, and get all the benefits of exercise. Talk about efficiency! Gas is expensive. Parking sucks, and sitting on your butt is not helping you. Leave your car at home and ride your bike to school. Win, win, win!

---

[14] Gomez-Pinilla, Fernando and Charles Hillman. "The Influence of Exercise on Cognitive Abilities." *Comprehensive Physiology* 3, no. 1 (January 2013): 403–428.

Have Fun: I can't really think of a time when I feel less stressed than when I am having fun. My stress seems to just disappear in the moment. Although engineering school will take up most of your time, don't forget to sprinkle in some real fun every week or so. And if you want to be extra efficient, combine your fun with your exercise. Racquetball served this purpose for me. There is something about smacking a ball as hard as you can then having it zoom back at your face at one hundred miles per hour that really takes the edge off. I played almost every Sunday during my school years. Do whatever works for you. It doesn't have to be exercise related as long as you're enjoying yourself: video games, fishing, go-karting, billiards, bowling, hiking, crafting. It doesn't matter. You know what you enjoy doing. Try to fit it into your schedule at least once a week. The only requirement is that a smile is on your face and you aren't thinking about school.

Your ability to reduce and manage your daily stress will be just as important as your performance in your classes. Too much stress will break anyone down eventually, so get on top of it early on. Really try to implement some or all of the suggestions above. It can really make all the difference.

Sustainable Schedule

Selecting your courses each semester is a very exciting time. Especially because it represents real tangible progress toward your graduation. However, this is one of the most crucial times to maintain realistic expectations of yourself. It can be very easy to overload your schedule, especially when selecting courses online can feel like you're simply shopping on the internet. "Just one or two more items in the shopping cart won't hurt. I can handle it!" Famous last words. Remember that it is always better to underdo it than overdo it when making your schedule, especially early in your schooling. The discouragement and overwhelming stress that can come with overloading yourself are not worth the pipe dream of graduating early.

Below is the approximate schedule that was recommended for my own bachelor's degree in mechanical engineering. (It has since changed, but the credit hour recommendations are generally the same.) It looks reasonable at first glance. But I only knew a handful of students who actually followed this plan and graduated within four years. Everyone else I knew took at least four and a half years (including myself). In reality, only 34 percent of all America engineering students graduate within four years.[15] The point is that a degree earned in five, six, or even ten years is just as valid as a degree earned in four. Of course, the ideal situation is for you to have no bills, no job, no kids, a personal chef, and fifty high school Advanced Placement credits. With that situation, graduating in four years is a reasonable expectation. But for the rest of us, four years might be a little less realistic. Your life situation may limit the amount of time you can dedicate to school. That is why you should look at your school's course schedule as more of a recommendation than a rule. Again, it all comes down to sustainability. Based on your personal situation, you must determine what is sustainable for you.

[15] American Society for Engineering Education. "Engineering by the Numbers: ASEE Retention and Time-to-Graduation Benchmarks for Undergraduate Engineering Schools, Departments and Programs." Washington, DC: Brian L. Yoder, 2016.

| YEAR 1 | | YEAR 2 | | YEAR 3 | | YEAR 4 | |
Fall - 15 Hrs	Spring - 15 Hrs	Fall - 17 Hrs	Spring - 15 Hrs	Fall - 15.5 Hrs	Spring - 16 Hrs	Fall - 15 Hrs	Spring - 18 Hrs
Intro to Design	Computational Problem Solving	Numerical Methods	Manufacturing	Seminar	Design of Mechanical Elements	Senior Design 1	Senior Design 2
Writing	Statics & Strenghts	Political Science	Thermo 1	Thermo 2	Ergonomics	Industrial Sefety	Sustainable Energy
Chemistry	Physics 1	Materials Science	Dynamics	Fluid Mechanics	Heat Transfer	Economics	Occupational Health
Chemistry Lab	Calculus 2	Physics 2	Electrical Engineering	Strengths 2	Mechatronics 2	History	Humanities
Calculus 1	Fine Arts	Ordinary Differential Equations	Calculus 3	Mechatronics 1	Partial Differeential Equations	Physical Education	Psychology

So how do you know what is sustainable? Without any previous experience to pull from, how can you know what is a reasonable expectation of yourself? Only you can answer this question, but I would err on the conservative side in the beginning because it can shield you from making some big mistakes. Your general education courses can lull you into a false sense of confidence. You must remind yourself that an engineering credit hour is not equal to a general education credit hour. Not even close. When transitioning to your engineering curriculum, the best approach is to enter with caution. You want to develop your experience without getting knocked out in the first round. So I recommend trying to sprinkle in some of your engineering and math courses as early as you can. This will give you a taste for the workload and what to expect moving forward. Then as you gain more and more experience, you will develop a feel for the level of workload you can handle sustainably.

Efficiency

Imagine spending an entire day trying to pull a large tree out of the ground with your bare hands. You yank and pull and strain as hard as you can, but the tree doesn't budge. How efficient was this activity? Another way to ask this same question is, "How much progress was made in relation to the time and energy spent?" In this case, the answer is a big fat zero. No progress equals 0 percent efficiency. I make this point to illustrate how time and energy input do not always translate into progress. Think of studying for an hour in front of the TV versus studying for an hour in a secluded office with no distraction. The same amount of time is invested in both scenarios. Which one do you think yields the most progress? It is only when you gain value from your invested time and energy that you achieve any level of progress and therefore efficiency. And because your time and energy are going to be quite limited while in school, your efficiency becomes extremely important.

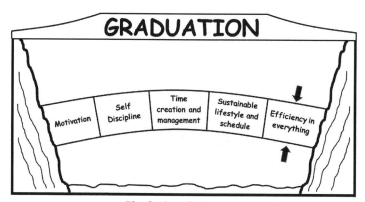

The Bridge of Graduation

Efficiency Equals Progress

The mathematical equation for efficiency is as follows:

$$Efficiency = Useful\ Work\ /\ Energy\ Input$$

In this case, useful work can be viewed as your progress. Let's define progress as anything that gets you closer to graduation. It could come in the form of passing a class, earning a good test score, finishing an assignment, understanding course material, decreasing stress, or freeing up extra time in your day. Progress is anything and everything that results in you getting closer to the thing you want most—a degree. In order to achieve any high level of progress, your efficiency must also be high. This can easily be seen by replacing useful work with progress and rearranging the equation.

$$Progress = Efficiency \times Energy\ Input$$

The above equation illustrates just how essential efficiency is to your progress. Low efficiency directly translates to low progress. The next obvious question is, "How do we maximize efficiency?" Let's rearrange the equation to find out.

$$Efficiency = Progress\ /\ Energy\ Input$$

As you can see, in order to increase efficiency, progress must be maximized while energy input is minimized. Pretty simple, right? Getting more while doing less is the name of the game. I understand that this may be overkill. However, I feel it's very important that you absorb the importance of your own efficiency. Your time and energy are extremely valuable, so they must be utilized well. The first step will be to make sure you are only pursuing activities that bring progress and to stop or limit the activities that bring no progress.

The Efficiency Filter

What is the best way to stop unwanted material in a constant flow? A filter! In this case, we need to stop inefficient behavior, so we will call this filter "the efficiency filter"! I know it's cheesy, but it's the simple cheesy stuff that is often the most effective. While you're in school, you will send all of your potential actions through your mental efficiency filter. The filter consists of two layers, each layer is just one simple question.

An action cannot make it to layer two without first passing through layer one. This means if there is no progress to be gained from an action, then it will not be considered actionable. If an action makes it to layer two, you must then determine how to gain the most value from it. This is a simple yet very effective way to increase your efficiency. By applying and acting on these questions, you will be simplifying your life by focusing your actions around one thing—progress. This simple technique worked wonders for me, and after a while, it will become automatic for you.

Maximizing Progress and Minimizing Input

Once an action is determined to contain some progress, it's time to determine how to gain the most progress from it. The easiest way to demonstrate how to do this is through some examples. Below you'll find a few ways you can make your day more efficient through maximizing progress while minimizing time and energy input. The list is by no means comprehensive and should be used as more of a catalyst for how you can apply your own ideas. Most of the items are very simple, but when practiced daily, they can really contribute to your efficiency.

Homework and Studying: Much of your progress is going to be gained from homework and studying. How can we increase efficiency here? Prioritize. Prioritize. Prioritize. We've already touched on how prioritizing can help relieve stress. But it can also increase your efficiency significantly for the same reasons. Not all activities are created equal, and some offer more progress than others. For instance, a ten-point homework assignment should probably hold a lower priority than studying for a one-hundred-point exam. Both items should be done, but the exam has the most progress associated with it, so it should come first. Pretty simple. The difficulty comes with acting *quickly* on your priorities. We would all rather do a small homework assignment than study our least favorite material all day. Human preference and emotion tend to get in the way of efficiency. This is why robots are so effective. They analyze the immediate situation, arrange in terms of priority, then act. No emotion included. Be more like a robot when establishing and acting on your priorities.

Lectures: Obviously, your class lectures provide progress. But how can we maximize that progress? One great way is to ask questions! I can't emphasize this one enough. If you are in class and you don't understand something, then *put your hand up*! Chances are good that someone else has the same question you have. And if not, who cares!? You're not in school for anyone but yourself. Don't you dare feel guilty or embarrassed to ask questions during a lecture. By leaving your questions unanswered, you are creating a snowball of inefficiency that will affect you for days. Not only will you struggle understanding that particular material for the rest of the lecture, but you will also struggle with the successive material and corresponding homework, which will probably result in a trip back to school during the professor's office hours—so much waste! All of which could have been avoided if you asked all of your questions during the lecture. Additionally, asking questions shows your professor that you are engaged in your learning. Professors love that!

- -

PRO TIP: Utilize Your Phone's Camera and microphone. During your lectures, it can be easy to forget your priorities. Many students get so caught up note-taking that they forget to actually understand the material first. You attend lectures to learn, not to take notes. Luckily for you, your phone has a nifty thing called a camera! Instead of struggling to keep up with everything your professor is writing on the board, just snap a picture or take a video. Spend your lecture time learning and asking questions, not mindlessly taking notes.

- -

Travel: Transportation is a necessary evil. Unfortunately, all of the places you'll need to be every day are not located in your home, so there will need to be some travel time. But what is the best way to minimize it? Combine trips! We already touched on this in chapter 5, but it's worth bringing up again. Try to combine all of your away-from-home activities (work, gym, grocery, school) into one trip. This can save quite a bit of time per week. Also, try to think ahead wherever you are. For instance, if you are already at the grocery store, think about what you may need in the next couple weeks and just get it now. This kind of foresight can really help save time and increase efficiency.

Hopefully, these few examples give you a general idea of how you can improve your efficiency almost anywhere. There are dozens more great ways to improve efficiency sprinkled throughout this book. Once you begin to consistently view your life through the lens of efficiency, thinking of ways to improve will become easier and more automatic. It has become a constant game for me. I honestly get hyped up if I can prepare my breakfast faster than I did the previous day. I know that's weird. The important thing is that you are constantly reassessing your own situation with new ways to increase progress and decrease input.

Quick Recap

Entering engineering school without a well-formulated plan would be irresponsible and counterproductive. Much like the tortoise who beat the hare, you must approach school in a way that is both sustainable and efficient. Begin with a sustainable mind-set, one which is grounded in realistic expectations, has good stress management, and can adapt quickly to setbacks. Next, you will need to develop a sustainable schedule that is practical and can be reasonably maintained for four to five years. And remember what is sustainable for someone else may not be sustainable for you. Don't get caught up in the game of comparison. Everyone can win this race; you just have to finish. Lastly, you need to develop a habit of constantly looking for ways to improve your own efficiency. Higher efficiency equals more progress. It's that simple. By taking these steps toward sustainability and efficiency, you will become a more resilient and effective student, one who will be well prepared to take on the challenges of this degree.

SEVEN

STUDYING PART I: WHERE AND WHEN

By failing to prepare, you are preparing to fail.
—Benjamin Franklin

Input and Outcome

What comes out is a direct result of what goes in. This is an inarguable law of nature. Every desired outcome must have the correct corresponding input. If your desired outcome is a green yard, the correct input would be sufficient water and sunshine. If the desired outcome is weight loss, the correct input would be diet and exercise. And if the desired outcome is a pepperoni pizza, the correct input would be dough, tomato sauce, cheese, and pepperoni, baked at 425 degrees for twenty-five minutes. Seems pretty simple, right? So what if your desired outcome is an engineering degree? What would be the correct input? I have three words for you: consistent, effective, studying. Say it with me. Consistent. Effective.

Studying. Three simple words, when implemented together, hold the key to your degree. If consistent effective studying goes in, then an engineering degree will come out—simple as that.

If it's so simple, then why do 40 percent of engineering students still fail to graduate? I'll answer that question with another. Do you ever remember learning *how* to study? I know I sure don't. I had to learn the hard way, which was through large amounts of failure, frustration, and effort. Many kids coming out of high school don't know anything about the psychology of learning or what it will really take to succeed at the collegiate level. There was never a class titled How to Learn 101, which is absolutely insane! How can we expect students to perform at high levels without first teaching them how to learn? This is akin to expecting a child to build a treehouse without first teaching them how to use a hammer. Sounds crazy, right? I believe this is a big reason why many students end up believing they aren't smart enough to succeed, when in reality, they have all of the tools they need, they were just never taught how to properly use them. This is why I've spent the last four chapters building the necessary foundation for you to become an effective studier. All of that motivation, self-discipline, time, sustainability, and efficiency get used here. Those five things are what students unknowingly lack the most.

Few things are as crucial to your success as becoming an effective studier, so it is essential that you understand how to use your brain to its full potential. And make no mistake, your brain has massive amounts of potential. It just needs to be harnessed and focused. The human brain is an extremely powerful and complex machine and needs to be treated as such. It is not just an empty canvas that you can hurl information at expecting it all to stick. You must feed it the right way. The next two chapters will teach you how to do just that. There is a lot to cover, so I have broken this subject into three parts: where to study, when to study, and how to study. This chapter will address the "where" and the "when," while the next chapter will cover the "how." The goal is to provide you with the tools and knowledge to unlock your brain's potential to learn new material and to retain information.

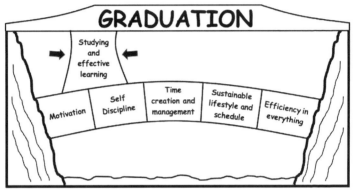

The Bridge of Graduation

Where to Study

Where you study will have a huge impact on how effective your study sessions will be. You should take it seriously. Many students needlessly fall behind in their studies because their primary study locations are too distracting or limited. This will be the place where you will effectively earn your degree, so do not take its location lightly. Just look at any high-performing athlete. The place where they train is a sanctuary—a temple that is totally dedicated to their craft. You need a location like this, a place that accommodates large amounts of time and focus with the sole purpose of effective studying. Trying to learn in a distracting location is like trying to dribble a basketball on grass. It is possible, but very difficult. Where you study should enhance your performance, not hinder it. Below I have listed the minimum requirements for a proper study location. Use them to determine if your own study location is adequate.

- -

Trying to learn in a distracting location is like trying to dribble a basketball on grass.

- -

Open 24-7: Many students are lured in by coffee shops, libraries, or cafes as good places to study. These places seem great at first glance. But unfortunately, they all have one huge drawback. They close. It's okay to study at these places every once in a while. But your primary study location should never close. It should be available twenty-four hours a day and seven days a week. The demand of your courses will not always be constant. One week you'll be able to keep a relatively normal study schedule and the next week you'll need to stay up until 3:00 a.m. Sunday and Monday. Your primary study location must accommodate this.

Distraction Free: The concepts and principles that you will be learning are difficult enough without an espresso machine running or a rambling television in the background. Your course material will require uninterrupted focus, so any and all distractions need to be eliminated. Your primary study location should be void of anything that has the potential to interrupt or hinder your focus.

Temptation Free: Oftentimes studying will be a grueling and challenging process. In response to this difficulty, your brain will look for anything else to do. It will try to tempt you into some other activity. "Oh, look! There's a lonely PlayStation over there! I should just play one little tiny game." And before you know it, your books are closed and you're three hours into the latest *Call of Duty* campaign. Don't let this happen. You need to remove these temptations from your study location before they have the chance to derail you.

PRO TIP: Utilize Airplane Mode. Your phone's ability to distract and tempt you is unmatched with notifications, videos, messages, emails, games...the list goes on and on. To help mitigate this, put your phone in airplane mode during your study sessions. This turns off data, Wi-Fi, and Bluetooth, effectively crippling your phone's ability to distract you.

Easily Accessible: Studying should not be made more difficult by an inconvenient location. Ideally, your primary study location should be in the same building where you live and somewhere that can be easily accessed at any time of day, preferably without getting in your car.

Dedicated: The kitchen is meant for cooking, the dining room is meant for eating, the bathroom is meant for grooming, and the family room is meant for leisure and socializing. None of these places are meant for studying. Your primary study location should be *dedicated* to studying and nothing else. When you're there, your only option is to study, period. I realize that this may be difficult to achieve for many students. However, there are some useful tricks to achieve the desired result regardless of your living situation presented later in this chapter.

Mentally and Physically Comfortable: Again, school will be challenging enough without having to study on a wooden bench in a poorly lit room. You're going to be spending hundreds of hours in this place. It is important that it make you feel physically and mentally comfortable while you're there. Seating, lighting, and desk space are some things to consider here.

Can Accommodate Others (or Not): Oftentimes it will be advantageous to work on assignments and projects with your peers. And other times you'll want to be completely alone. Your primary study location should accommodate these two scenarios. It should have room for three to four people while also providing complete solitude when necessary.

Mental Cues

How many times have you tried to study in bed only to end up unintentionally asleep, or sat down on the living room couch with the intention of doing some homework only to find yourself watching TV or playing video games? If you answered yes to either of these scenarios, you're not alone. We are all triggered into action by sensory cues. When you see, hear, or smell something familiar, your mind automatically associates that sight, sound, or smell with its corresponding action. The bed equals sleep, the living room couch equals TV or video games, and the kitchen counter equals eating, drinking, and socializing. This is why it can be so difficult to study in your bed, living room, or kitchen. These rooms are full of sensory cues signaling your mind to do something else.

Your primary study location should work with you, not against you. When you're there, it should feel like it's time to work, not play, relax, or eat. I realize that it is rare for a student to have a huge private office in their home or apartment. Most dorm rooms are basically a glorified closet. Chances are good that the only room students truly have to themselves is their bedroom. But don't worry, most of the steps above can be accomplished with some noise-canceling headphones and a lamp—yes, a lamp.

As stated above and in chapter 4, the mind can be programmed using simple cues. Once a cue is established, your mind responds with the programmed action. With this knowledge, you can effectively turn any room into your primary study location as long as the designated cue is established and used correctly. I will demonstrate with an example. Let's say you live in the dorms at your university, where your bedroom, living room, bathroom, kitchen, and office are basically mixed into one multipurpose room. Based on what has already been described, this seems like a nightmare studying situation, with your television, refrigerator, bicycle, PlayStation, and bed all calling to you at once, tempting you to take their corresponding actions. In order to overcome these already established cues, you must establish a new cue. In this case, the cue will be a simple lamp—a study lamp.

When it's time to study, sit down at your desk and turn the study lamp on. While the study lamp is on, you are committed to studying and focusing intensely. When your session is over or it's time to take a break, you turn the study lamp off. With consistency, your mind will start to recognize this lamp as its study cue. While the study lamp is on, the other distractions in the room become less powerful. This may sound crazy, but it works. In a study at the University of Hawaii, a psychology professor had half of his class establish a study cue and had the other half do nothing. The half that implemented a study cue did an average of a full letter grade higher than the other half.[16] Those are pretty remarkable results. Just by implementing some simple psychology, you can turn a nonideal study location into your sanctuary. The most important thing is that the cue is used only when you're studying. If you are not studying, do not use the cue. The efficacy of this process depends on it.

The importance of location may sound silly, but you should trust me on this one. Your environment can either enhance your ability to perform or inhibit it. You will have enough on your plate without having to deal with unnecessary distractions. You're going to be spending a significant amount of time studying, so be sure to take steps early to secure an adequate study location for yourself. You need a sanctuary where you can focus freely without distraction or temptation. Once you have this place, it's time to get to work.

When to Study

When you are cooking a good meal, success requires more than just having all of the ingredients. You must also know how to put them together. You don't just mash everything into a pot and turn up the heat. The recipe really develops by applying precision and direction. The ingredients should have precise quantities that are combined at particular times during the process. Without proper quantities and timing, the resulting meal will suffer in quality. Becoming an effective studier is a lot like this. Trying to study for six hours straight on a

---

[16] Psychology Professor Marty Lobdell's lecture on the science behind taking breaks and study queues - https://www.youtube.com/watch?v=IlU-zDU6aQ0&t

Monday night right after work with no break is akin to just mashing all your ingredients into that pot. The result will be less than ideal. However, if you were to apply some precise quantities and timing, your results would actually improve greatly. This section will show how precision and timing can massively improve your effectiveness while studying and demonstrate how to apply them.

Taking Breaks

The average college freshman can effectively focus for only about twenty minutes at a time.[17] Once a student pushes beyond this initial period, their ability to absorb and retain material drops off quickly and significantly. You could study for six hours straight but really only benefit from the first half hour or so. This is because your productivity is not linearly proportional to the time you spend studying. A graph of what this can look like is shown below.

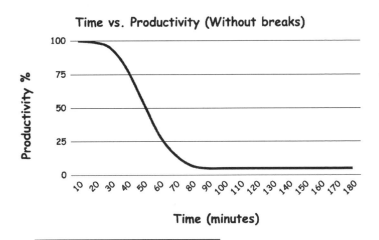

[17] Korn, James H., and Karen Wilson. "Attention During Lectures: Beyond Ten Minutes." *Teaching of Psychology* 34, no. 2 (June 2007): 85–89.

As you can see in the graph, once you surpass that first section of high productivity, your performance drops like a rock.[18] Attempting to continue after your initial productive period is almost a waste of time. Your ability to focus and be productive declines so rapidly that you might as well be staring at Egyptian hieroglyphics. It is important to note that everyone's productive period is a little different. Yours may be longer or shorter than average. But one thing is for sure: we all hit that wall eventually. Your mind starts to wander. Your attention drifts. And before you know it, you're on your phone doing whatever. We have all experienced it. But the question is, can we do anything about it? Fortunately, the answer is yes! It's very simple … take a break.

When you exercise, your muscles can only last so long before their strength diminishes. However, just by taking a short ten to fifteen-minute break, your muscles can basically recover back to full strength. Your brain is very similar. Your ability to focus and be productive can easily be recharged by taking a short effective break. A graph of what this can look like is shown below. The gaps represent each small study break. Notice how productivity almost completely recovers after each break.

---

[18] Ariga, Atsunori, and Alejandro Lleras. "Brief and Rare Mental 'Breaks' Keep You Focused: Deactivation and Reactivation of Task Goals Preempt Vigilance Decrements." *Cognition* (2011).

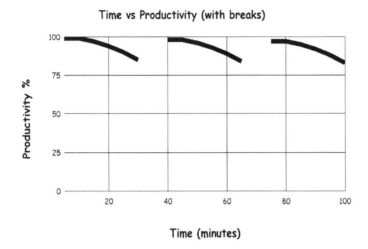

Time vs Productivity (with breaks)

Time (minutes)

When I was in school, it took me a while to recognize the power of an effective break. They seemed very counterproductive to me. It felt like taking a break was just being lazy and wasting time. But once I noticed the positive effect it had on my performance, I was completely sold. I began regularly taking ten-minute breaks every hour. After a good break, my brain felt recharged and ready for more. [19]

Numerous studies have confirmed this phenomenon.[20] Your brain responds positively to change. If it is subjected to the same task for too long, it will quickly become exhausted and somewhat desensitized to the material, therefore making

---

[19] Great article on the power of mental downtime - Ferris Jabr,"Why Your Brain Needs More Downtime" Last modified October 15, 2013, https://www.scientifi-camerican.com/article/mental-downtime/

[20] Jinyi Long, Quiyou Xie, M. A. Urbin, Liqing Liu, Ling Weng, Xiaoqi Huang, RonghaoYu, Yuanqing Li, and Ruiwang Huang. "Distinct Interactions between Fronto-Parietal and Default Mode Networks in Impaired Consciousness." *Scientific Reports* 6, 38866 (December 2016).

it almost impossible to absorb or retain anything new. Much like your senses. If they are subjected to constant stimuli for too long, the stimulus will seem to disappear after a while. Think about when you first smell the sweet aroma of cookies baking. Your nose is firing on all cylinders, sending those sweet chocolatey messages to your brain. But after just a short time, the once strong scent fades to a much less intense experience. However, if you were to step outside for a few minutes, your sense of smell would reset and those cookies would smell just as sweet as the first time you came in. You can think of your brain in the very same way when studying. In order for it to maintain a high level of focus, it will need to be reset on a regular basis by taking a good break. Below are the three most important ingredients to an effective break.

Unfocus Your Mind: In order for your brain to perform at its best for long periods of time, you actually must unfocus your mind regularly. During your break times, don't focus on anything. Let your mind wander and relax. When you unfocus your mind, it will subconsciously go to work making new memories and creating ideas. We've all experienced this. When you are seemingly doing and thinking about nothing, an idea or solution will just pop into your brain out of nowhere. These occurrences are not a coincidence. They are enabled by the unfocusing of your mind.

Move Your Body: I shouldn't have to sell you again on the benefits of exercise. But just in case, I will anyway.

⇒ **Mood Boost:** After exercise, your brain will increase the production of the feel-good hormones, serotonin and dopamine.

⇒ **Increases Energy:** Movement increases the circulation of blood and oxygen throughout the body. A solid ten-minute walk can give you up to two hours of energy!

⇒ **Decreases Stress and Anxiety:** Even small amounts of exercise can lower your resting heart rate and release built-up tension.

Change Your Environment: Reset your mind by getting away from your study area—maybe go outside for a few minutes. Changing your environment will enable your mind to recharge and reset. Below is a list of effective break-time activities guaranteed to reset and recharge your brain.

⇒ Go for a short walk outside.
⇒ Take a short shower.
⇒ Go for a short bicycle ride.
⇒ Do some push-ups or sit-ups.
⇒ Take a fifteen to twenty-minute power nap.
⇒ Meditate.
⇒ Play with your dog or cat.
⇒ Make a healthy snack.
⇒ Clean your room.
⇒ Get up and stretch.
⇒ Be creative and doodle.

The possibilities are really endless. But do try to stay away from social media and the internet. Screen time will not give your brain what it needs during a break. Stick to the three ingredients and get creative. It won't be long before you notice the huge positive impact taking a break has on your productivity. The next time you sit down for a study session, take note of how long you can focus productively. It may be twenty minutes or it may be sixty minutes. But when your mind does eventually begin to wander and the fog sets in, this is your cue to take a break and let your mind relax and recover for a few minutes. Although this technique is simple, the advantages are too great to ignore. Trust me, as your study sessions get longer and longer, which they will, implementing regular breaks will be vital to maintaining the focus your courses will require. For more on the power of taking breaks, I recommend checking out Professor Marty Lobdell's "Study Less Study Smart" lectures on YouTube.

Spaced Repetition

I want you to think back to the last time you crammed for an exam. How did you perform? And more importantly, how long did you retain what you learned? If you had to take that same exam today, would you pass it? I'm willing to bet that you probably wouldn't do very well. But why? Why do some concepts become implanted into our minds forever while other concepts seem to be temporary? It all comes down to how they were learned in the first place.

In psychology, the term "spacing effect" refers to the phenomenon in which learning is enhanced by the spreading out of learning sessions over time compared to cramming all learning into one session. This effect was first observed in 1885 by German psychologist Herman Ebbinghaus.[21] In his groundbreaking study, Ebbinghaus demonstrated that spacing out learning over several days can reduce the time it takes to

---

[21] Ebbinghaus, Herman. *Über das Gedächtnis. Untersuchungen zur experimentellen Psychologie* (*Memory: A Contribution to Experimental Psychology*). New York: Dover, 1885.

effectively learn by half. This finding has since been replicated by several more recent studies.[22] What's even more significant is a recent study in the Proceeding of the National Academy of Sciences (PNAS) concluded that spacing out study sessions will also convert material to long-term memory much more effectively.[23] This study showed that in order to create solid long-lasting learning, some amount of forgetting must take place. Implementing gaps in between sessions will force you to remember and effectively relearn the material each session. This in turn strengthens and solidifies the learned material more and more each session.

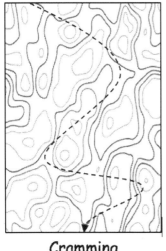 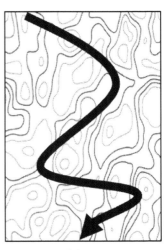

Cramming   Spaced Repetition

---

[22] Shaughnessy, John J. "Long-Term Retention and the Spacing Effect in Free-Recall and Frequency Judgments." *The American Journal of Psychology* 90, no. 4 (December 1977): 587-598.

[23] Aziz, Wajeeha, Wen Wang, Sebnem Kesaf, Alsayed Abdelhamid Mohamed, Yugo Fukazawa, and Ryuichi Shigemoto. "Distinct Kinetics of Synaptic Structural Plasticity, Memory Formation, and Memory Decay in Massed and Spaced Learning." *Proceedings of the National Academy of Sciences* 111 (1) E194–E202 (December 2013).

A good analogy for this is to think of establishing a new trail in a thick jungle. In order to create a truly distinguishable path, you must travel the same path hundreds of times. Every time the path is traveled, it helps the trail become a little more permanent. However, if it were only to be traveled once or twice (similar to cramming), it would hardly look like a trail at all, making it much more difficult to find and travel in the future. By spacing out your learning, not only will you decrease the overall time to learn, but you will also create much stronger and longer-lasting memories.

The first and most crucial step in implementing spaced repetition into your own studies is to establish a sustainable schedule, one that isn't overloaded and has your priorities clearly established (see chapter 6). The next step is to learn your course material at the same pace as it is presented. This may sound like an obvious statement. But you'd be surprised how often students learn (or attempt to learn) the material for the first time the night before an exam. That was me during the first couple of years as an undergrad. Late-night cramming sessions on the eve of an exam were my go-to strategy. Little did I know that this way of learning is very high risk and is not conducive to long-term retention whatsoever. It's no surprise that my GPA during that time was a cool 2.4.

It wasn't until I was in graduate school that I really started implementing spaced repetition. I learned and practiced the material at the same pace that my professors taught it. Instead of just blasting through homework as fast as I could, I took my time and used my homework assignments to learn and absorb the concepts. I started my assignments the same night they were assigned, so I had time to get with my professors to clarify my understanding. By the time an exam came around, studying was so much less stressful because it was really more of a review at that point. Lo and behold, I earned a 3.8 GPA during my master's degree coursework. By spacing out my learning and giving myself adequate time to properly absorb and master my course material, I was able to perform at a much higher level.

Procrastination

Now would probably be a good time to talk about the mortal enemy of spaced repetition—procrastination, every student's guilty pleasure. We've all done it. We've neglected that ten-page paper until the night before it was due or stayed up till 4:00 a.m. cramming for an exam because we chose to hang out with our friends all weekend. Sound familiar? We all do it, and our grades almost always suffer from it. This is all known. But if we all know the detrimental effects of procrastination, why does everyone still do it? The answer is because the payoff for procrastinating is immediate. The payoff for not procrastinating is usually much further in the future and therefore less motivating. "You're telling me that if I don't do my homework, I can continue to play video games right now?" We make the choice to procrastinate, then we have that quick little mental pep talk that goes something like, "It's okay; I'll stay up late and get it done tonight," or "I already know that material pretty well; I don't need to study," or "I can take a zero on that assignment. Homework is only ten percent of my overall grade anyway." Is this sounding familiar?

The effects of procrastination may seem small. But the decisions build upon each other until the effects are quite large. One missed assignment becomes four. One missed study session becomes a bad test score. A bad test score becomes a failed course. The immediate payoff of procrastination can be very tempting and it can easily become habitual. And if there is one habit that will derail your success in engineering, it's the "p-word." Procrastination will make any sort of spaced repetition or consistent studying impossible, which is why it is crucial that you take steps early on to kill any habit of procrastination. I know, it is easier said than done. However, there is a very effective technique that can help stop procrastination in its tracks.

The Pomodoro Technique

An assignment or project not yet started can be quite daunting. Just the thought of the effort it will require can be intimidating, which explains why procrastination is usually at its strongest when you're at the beginning of a new task. The unknown is at its largest. It can feel like you're standing at the bottom of Mount Everest. Just looking up at its never-ending magnitude makes you want to run for cover. It seems totally unsurmountable. But what if you were able to change your perspective? What if, instead of seeing the entire mountain, you only saw one small thirty-minute block of work? That is much less intimidating, don't you think? This idea is what the Pomodoro Technique is based on. The technique was created by Francesco Cirillo in the late 1980s, with the intention of breaking down one large task with an unknown end point into small defined blocks of work with very specific end points. It is very simple and yet extremely powerful (the best techniques always are) because it changes how you *perceive* the task. And when your perception changes, everything changes. The task magically transforms from something big and intimidating into something very accomplishable.

Implementing the Pomodoro Technique is simple. Begin by selecting a task that you've been struggling to start, maybe a homework assignment, reading a textbook, a term project, or a lab report. It could really be anything that has pushed you to procrastinate. Once you've decided on your task, set aside

129

one thirty-minute block of time to work on that task. Make sure to actually set a timer for those thirty minutes. You can use your phone or an old kitchen timer. There are also several apps that work great. Just type in "Pomodoro" into the app store search bar and take your pick. My personal favorite is an app called Tide (I used it while writing this book). Then once the timer is up, you're done! Congratulations, you have completed one Pomodoro. Yup, it's that simple. Now you can either be finished or take a small break and begin another Pomodoro cycle. You can then link as many Pomodoro cycles together as you like. And after just a few Pomodoro cycles, you will have made a notable dent in your task.

Pomodoro Cycle

30	10	30	10	30	10	30	DONE

WORK	BREAK

As the dent gets larger and larger, the task will become easier and easier to continue to work on. It's also no coincidence that the Pomodoro Technique syncs up perfectly with implementing short breaks in your work. Additionally, your Pomodoro cycle does not need to be thirty minutes; it can be longer or shorter based on your personal performance. Just make sure you're focused and working intensely while the timer is going. I realize this sounds too simple to be this effective, but, trust me, this will cure your procrastination. The true power comes from how it will transform your perception of the task from something huge and painful into something small and easy. This makes all the difference.

Quick Recap

Every desired outcome must have the correct corresponding input. If an engineering degree is what you want to come out, consistent effective studying must go in. It begins with a proper study location. The place where you study will essentially be where you earn your degree. It should enable your success, not hinder it. Ideally, it should not be the same place where you sleep, eat, or play. Your study location should be easily accessible and open 24–7. It should be a dedicated location free of distraction and temptation. Once you have an established study location, take advantage of effective mental cues to enhance your focus and subvert temptation. Next, implement proper timing throughout your studying strategy. Begin by recognizing the importance of relaxing your mind. Implement regular and effective break times throughout your study sessions. Learn more effectively and increase retention by taking advantage of spaced repetition. Learn at the same pace that the material is taught. And, last but not least, kill the virus of procrastination and change your perception of difficult tasks by implementing the Pomodoro Technique. How do you build a house? Brick by brick.

EIGHT

STUDYING PART 2: HOW

A man is but the product of his thoughts. What he thinks he
becomes.
—Mahatma Gandhi

Replace "Can't" with "How"

Too often students blame their struggles on supposed inherent
capabilities. They think that if they struggle to comprehend
something now, then they always will—and that somehow
their mental competence is constant and unchanging. This is
just plain false! If there is one point that I want to make crystal
clear with this book, it is that your ability to comprehend and
retain material is *not set in stone*! It can be improved and enhanced over time. You must know and believe this. Because
as your academic curriculum becomes more strenuous, there
will be times when you may be tempted to question your own
mental and physical capabilities. You *must* avoid this. I can't
stress this point enough. Because once you begin to question

your own capabilities, all of your mental doors to improvement and progress will begin to close. Your brain will switch from a "creative attack" mode to a "passive defeated" mode. Talk about shooting yourself in the foot!

So as we get into the "how" of studying, the very first step is to replace the word "can't" with the word "how." When you're struggling to understand any material, you should never say, "I can't understand this." Instead you should always ask, "How do I understand this?" This is an essential mental shift that every student *must* make. Never ever question *if you can*. Always ask *how you can* instead. By asking *how*, you are cultivating creativity and progress. Your mind will automatically go to work figuring new and different ways to proceed. This will be crucial as you begin to develop your study habits, especially because everyone learns a little differently. Proper learning is a very individual and systematic process, so you'll need to iterate your process until you find what works for you, then stick to it. This chapter will get you started. In the pages ahead, you will learn the most effective and scientifically backed study techniques along with the ways that I found success in studying.

How to Study

How do you know if a particular study session was effective? Is it how much time you've spent? Is it how many pages you've read or notes you've taken? These may seem like reliable metrics. But I think we have all experienced long study sessions where we've spent hours going through dozens and dozens of pages without ever really absorbing anything. Effective studying really boils down to three things: comprehension, application, and retention. Did you truly comprehend and understand the material? Can you apply the material? And did you retain the material? The answer must be yes to all three of these questions in order for a study session to be truly effective.

Sometimes you can comprehend material but struggle with all the ways it can be applied. Sometimes you can apply material robotically without really comprehending any of it. Yet other times you've retained material that you don't fully comprehend. All of these scenarios are equally useless, especially when it's exam time. That is why this chapter will be broken up into three parts: Comprehension, application, and retention. Part 1 will explore different ways you can make comprehending and understanding new material easier. Part 2 will discuss the importance of being able to apply what you have learned. And part 3 will discuss how to transfer that newly understood material into long-term memory.

- -
Never ever question "if you can." Always ask "how you can" instead.
- -

Part 1 — Comprehension

Comprehension equals understanding. It is where learning begins. It is the foundation on which your mental capability is built. In construction, a building is only as strong as its foundation. The stronger the foundation, the bigger the building it can support. A weak foundation can only support so much weight before crumbling. This was the story of my first few semesters in engineering school. I failed several courses and was barely clinging to a C average. I can now honestly say that the primary cause of my dismal performance was my neglect in building a proper foundation of comprehension. I never took the time to really read the textbook or do research to understand underlying theories and principles. I would memorize specific equations and learn how to perform only certain applications of a given topic. Then I would just hope those types of problems showed up on the exam.

As you can imagine, my GPA did not benefit from this strategy. After several failed courses and discouraging exam scores, I began to realize that something needed to seriously change, or else I was about to become another dropout statistic. I did not invest nearly enough time comprehending and understanding the underlying material. Don't make this mistake. You must take the time to build an adequate foundation of comprehension if you expect to have sustained success.

Imagine a large tree with several branches. The trunk of the tree represents the core theory and principles supporting a given topic. The branches represent all of the different applications that stem from those core principles. In order to achieve true comprehension of any given topic, you must begin with the trunk. You must mentally absorb and understand the core ideas before moving out onto any branches. If you only study one application of any topic, you're basically isolating yourself on one branch of the tree hoping that your professor only tests you on that specific application. However, if you start at the trunk and actually take the time to absorb the core theory and principles that support the entire topic, it won't matter what shows up on an exam. Because by understanding the core theory and principles, you will be equipped with the tools to tackle any application.

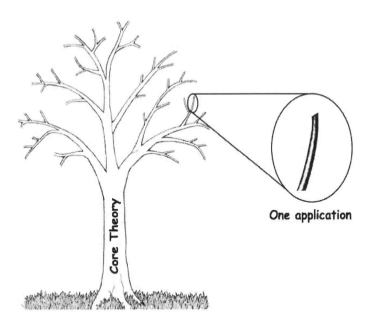

One application

Read Your Damn Textbook

Once I began to take my lack of comprehension seriously, I made sure that I fully understood the core theory and principles before practicing a single problem. To put it simply, I sat my butt down and read. I opened my textbook and read every single page that was relevant. If I did not understand something, I researched it online, emailed my professor or TA, or contacted peers until I understood the material. I would not turn the page until the material was understood and absorbed into my brain. As you can imagine, this process often required multiple sessions of several hours. But let me tell you, it was beyond worth it. In fact, I would say this was the single most beneficial change I made when it came to studying.

I know that sounds incredibly simple. But it blows me away how many students don't thoroughly read through their textbooks. They either skim the highlighted parts or just go through the example problems. Come on, people! This behavior is akin to just rolling the dice on your degree! The textbook is the *source material*. Why would you not start there? The purpose of your lectures, labs, and notes is to help you understand the material in your textbook. It is what your courses are built around! I know it's not the flashiest or most revolutionary recommendation, but I can guarantee you it will be one of the most effective changes you make. *Read your damn textbook!*

SQ3R Method (Survey, Question, Read, Recite, Review)

How many times have you read a few pages of a textbook, then realized you have absolutely no idea what you just read? Don't worry; you're not alone. Engineering textbooks aren't what one would call page-turners. While they may be very interesting, they do require a large amount of focus and effort on your part. On a funny side note, while I was in school, I literally read my thermodynamics textbook out loud to my girlfriend to help her sleep, and it worked like a charm. Luckily there are some strategies that can help increase your level of comprehension while reading. My favorite is the SQ3R method, which stands for Survey, Question, Read, Recite, Review. The method was first developed by American education philosopher Francis P. Robinson in 1946 in his book *Effective Study*. SQ3R is an active learning method designed to keep the reader engaged and focused on the material being read. And with the additional effort comes a much greater understanding of the material. Let's look at each step a little closer.

Survey: The first step of SQ3R is to briefly survey the chapter or section you're about to read. Take note of the section headings, charts, example problems, summaries, and anything else you recognize from your lectures. Remember this is only a brief skim. Do not read every word. This exercise should only take several minutes. By surveying what you are about to read, you will prime your mind to recognize and respond more effectively to the material you're about to read.

Read and Question: Now it's time to go back and read every word—*every single word.* Take it slowly and don't skip over anything. If you've finished a page and realize your mind was elsewhere, stop yourself, refocus, and reread that page. Then as you read, you should constantly be asking questions and writing them down. "Does this definition make sense to me? Where did that variable come from? Does this graph make sense? Is this consistent with what my professor discussed in class?" Then as you ask yourself questions, you should immediately seek out the answers. You could look online, reference your notes, or email your professor and classmates. By asking plenty of questions, you will stay actively engaged in the reading. Also, remember to take plenty of breaks (reference chapter 7). This should not be a quick process. Let it take as long as it needs.

Note: Typically, the question step comes before the read step, but I think it's more effective to ask questions as you actually read. This way the questions you ask are more informed and relevant.

Recite: Who says talking to yourself isn't cool? It is well established that verbalizing text helps secure content to memory.[24] So, as you read, talk to yourself and ask questions out loud. And most importantly, try to answer those questions in your own words. Successfully converting concepts into your own words is a great way to prove your understanding of a subject.

Review: Lastly, it's time to review what you have learned. This step should help to solidify what you read and clear up any lingering questions. Go through the questions that you wrote down while reading and try to answer them without referencing the text. Go through each section and try to summarize each major point or definition. Work through the practice problems on your own without solutions. Remember there is a big difference between recognition and recollection. Just because you recognize a highlighted equation does not mean you can recall its meaning and application. Don't trick yourself. During the review, make sure you have actually remembered material.

The SQ3R method is so effective because it demands action. By asking questions, doing research, and reciting material, your mind will stay engaged and present in the reading, therefore much more open to comprehension. Again, I cannot stress enough how important it is to read and understand the material in your textbook. Class lectures, labs, and homework are all based on what is presented in your textbooks. The textbook is the source material, and it should be treated as such. Do not make the huge mistake of thinking you can neglect the reading.

---

[24] Forrin, Noah D. and Colin M. MacLeod. "This Time It's Personal: The Memory Benefit of Hearing Oneself." *Memory* 26, no. 4 (2018): 574–579.

Make Material Meaningful

Relating something that is unknown to something that is known creates a pathway to true comprehension. And true comprehension is the bridge between imitation and actual understanding. It is the difference between just memorizing the steps to solve a problem and actually understanding what an equation is modeling. This is what you should be striving for while studying. You want the ideas and concepts to actually *mean* something to you. This is how your knowledge actually becomes useful. Your mind should begin to look like a huge spider web of connections between different pieces of knowledge. With more connections comes stronger understanding and increased ability to comprehend new material.

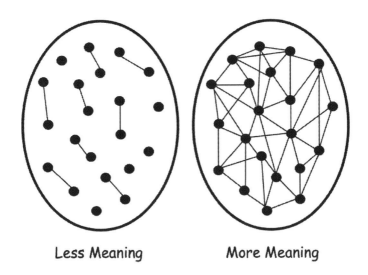

Less Meaning   More Meaning

Many times, creating meaning for unknown material is very simple. For example, when I was first introduced to the idea of angular momentum, I really struggled to comprehend it. It just did not make sense in my mind. But once I applied

140

the idea to my experience while riding a bicycle, it clicked immediately. Using the concept of angular momentum, I was now able to understand how it allowed me to stay upright while riding. Awesome! So I was able to explain my real-life experience with an abstract idea in physics. It was exactly what my brain needed as it tried to connect new information to something I already had stored, like a new piece to an unfinished puzzle. This is a very simple yet extremely powerful exercise. Because once it is accomplished, you are then able to apply the new idea to other known situations in your mind. It becomes a part of your mental toolbox, ready to be called upon at any time. The important point here is that the meaningful relation does not always need to come from your previous course material. It can come just as easily from simple everyday experiences, like riding a bike! So, when you find yourself stuck and unable to comprehend a new idea, try to give it meaning with something that you already know. If you are unable, work backward until you arrive at something that you can relate to. Then move forward again, making new connections as you go.

- -

True comprehension is the bridge between imitation and actual understanding.

- -

Use Your Lifelines

There will be times while studying when you feel like you're smashing your face up against a brick wall. You'll feel like a baby sloth trying to comprehend space travel or like your textbook must be missing a few pages. The important thing is that you not let yourself get discouraged in these situations. You must understand that the pathway to your comprehension *always* exists. You just need to find it. These moments are normal, and they happen to everyone all the time. However, your understanding won't always come from your textbook and notes. Oftentimes you will require additional resources. I like to call these additional resources your lifelines. Below you'll find some of the most useful supplemental resources that can aid you on your way to true comprehension.

Professor / TA: *Never ever* hesitate to contact your professor or TA whenever you have a question or are struggling to understand something. Take advantage of your professor's office hours. If you can't make their office hours, email them. Email them multiple times if needed. I literally emailed my professors almost daily while in graduate school. Part of being an effective teacher is being responsive to any and all questions. Most professors are very responsive and will be happy to help. Unfortunately, you will run into the less helpful type from time to time—professors who think their time is too valuable to waste on undergraduate inquiries. In these situations, don't be intimidated. Email them anyway. If they aren't responsive, don't hesitate to go to the dean. Remember, you are the customer. You are paying for their services. This is your education and you are paying good money for it. You should get what you pay for.

It is so important that you get the most out of your face-to-face meetings with any teacher. Many students leave meetings prematurely or hold back because they feel intimidated or exposed. If you have no idea what the hell you're doing, the last thing you should do is stay quiet about it. You are only hurting yourself if you hold back. Be honest and upfront about your ignorance and request that they work with you until you understand. Always remember that *you are the customer*, not the other way around. If you leave a meeting with remaining questions, then you only have yourself to blame.

- -

PRO TIP: Get to Know Your Professors. Don't let yourself be just another student in the eyes of your professors. There is a lot to be gained by creating actual relationships with them—the kind of relationship where they recognize you, know your name, and have a vested interest in your personal success. These relationships are built outside of class during office hours, tutoring sessions, and email conversations. Not only will these relationships help you in your classes but they are also a great start to your professional network. Who knows, you may even be asking some of them to write letters of recommendation for graduate school.

- -

Peers: Your fellow classmates are incredibly valuable resources, so don't ignore them. Get to know as many of your peers as you can, and make friends early, ideally with people who are driven like you. Don't waste time with people who aren't serious. Get as many phone numbers as you can. Everyone is going through the same thing, so chances are good that at least one of them will be able to help you in a time of need. On the flip side, always make sure to help others when you can. One-way relationships don't last very long, so be sure to contribute to your study group.

During my undergrad, I developed a study group of around twelve people. We all had our own strengths and weaknesses. But we all contributed and helped each other as much as possible. I know it can be hard sometimes to develop new relationships. But trust me, the relationships you create with your classmates will be some of the most important and long-lasting relationships you will ever make.

Khan Academy: www.khanacademy.org. If you've never heard of Khan Academy, do yourself a favor and check it out. Khan Academy is a free online education platform specializing in math and science. I turned to Khan's videos weekly during my undergraduate degree. His videos are simple, and his teaching style is very effective. They offer videos covering almost every math, science, and engineering topic imaginable. Khan Academy is an absolute must for new students, especially for your core math and science courses. Khan Academy also comes in app form, making it accessible from anywhere.

Google: www.google.com. It's difficult to imagine a world without Google. The entire collection of human knowledge is at your fingertips. I'm sure you already have plenty of experience with Google. But here are a few tips that may help while you're searching.

⇒ Try Google Scholar. It's a more specific search engine that searches scholarly articles, theses, abstracts, books, and other publications.

⇒ Try phrasing your search differently if you aren't happy with the results.

⇒ Use quotes to search for an exact phrase.

⇒ Use the built-in define function. Just type in "DEFINE: topic."

YouTube: www.youtube.com. YouTube is quickly becoming the go-to source for learning basically anything. It's not hard to believe when you learn that three hundred hours of video are uploaded to the site every minute! If you're having trouble understanding literally anything, there is a good chance that you will find several explanations and examples on YouTube.

Tutors: Odds are good that your school offers free tutoring, especially for math. Usually, tutors are graduate students or professional volunteers. This is a free resource, so don't hesitate to take advantage of it. Private tutoring is also an option, especially if you're looking for a more one-on-one experience. A quick internet search should provide several tutors in your area. Another good option is Varsity Tutors (www.varsitytutors.com). Varsity Tutors is an online service that connects you to tutors in your area. It's basically the Uber of the tutoring world. Keep in mind that private tutoring typically costs $20 to $50 per hour. But that's money well spent if it gets you the results you want.

Chegg: www.chegg.com. You may have heard of Chegg due to its explosion in popularity over the past several years. The website's textbook solutions, online tutoring, and Q and A forums have become many students' go-to resource for homework help. Much of your homework will come straight out of your textbook. There is a good chance that Chegg will have nearly every worked-out solution uploaded to their site. This can be a very valuable learning tool as long as you are actually using the solutions to learn. Unfortunately, this is not what many students use Chegg for. The appeal of getting their homework done in twenty minutes, as opposed to four hours, by copying down answers is too attractive for many to resist. So be careful. This behavior will lead to poor exam scores and in some cases a trip to the dean's office. Most schools are cracking down big time on students who are "Chegging" their way through homework. If you neglect what you are responsible for learning, you are cheating not only yourself but all the future users of your engineering as well.

Think about it this way. Would you cross a bridge designed by an engineer who cheated on all of his or her homework? I didn't think so. Don't be that engineer. If you're going to use Chegg, use it how it was intended to be used—to enhance your learning, not to replace it. Also, remember that access to the material currently requires a monthly subscription of $14.95/month. Similar services include Quizlet (www.quizlet.com) and Course Hero (www.coursehero.com).

If you neglect what you are responsible for learning, you are cheating not only yourself but all the future users of your engineering as well.

Wolfram Alpha: www.wolframalpha.com. Wolfram Alpha is a very powerful computational engine that can basically solve any math problem you throw at it. It will show the answer and some additional data for free. But to get the full step-by-step solution, you'll need to subscribe to the service, which is currently $4.75/month. The service is also available in app form for $2.99. Additionally, Wolfram Alpha offers helpful and organized search results for almost any other topic. I will stress the same warning here as I did for Chegg. Having fully worked-out solutions can be a very helpful learning tool as long as they are used responsibly.

Symbolab: www.symbolab.com is primarily a math computational engine similar to Wolfram Alpha with a few differences. The step-by-step solutions are free online, as long as you're okay with a few ads here and there. The app is free. However, it costs $14.99 per year to unlock the step-by-step solutions and eliminate the ads. Also, the user interface does not require knowledge of math syntax, unlike Wolfram Alpha.

Photomath: Your phone's camera just became your best friend. This free app can solve almost any simple math problem with a quick point from your camera. There are other apps that offer similar features, but this one seems to work the best. It provides step-by-step solutions and clean explorable graphs. You can also manually input problems. Currently, the app boasts an average rating of 4.8 out of 5 stars with over 600,000 reviews.

Wikipedia: www.wikipedia.com. Wikipedia has proven itself to be a reliable resource for just about anything. The website is currently the largest and most popular reference on the internet. Its content is constantly updated and monitored to ensure the most accurate and up-to-date information possible. The service is also available in app form.

Stack Exchange: www.stackexchange.com. Stack Exchange is a question-and-answer based platform made up of a large number of smaller topic-based communities, the largest of which is the programming community, Stack Overflow (www.stackoverflow.com). Users can ask questions and browse forums for helpful and popular answers while also contributing educated content along the way. The best and most helpful answers will rise to the top.

Engineering Toolbox: www.engineeringtoolbox.com. This website contains almost everything you could ever need as an engineer. It serves as a unique collection of all the quirky and obscure tools, tables, equations, definitions, conversions, and examples that any engineering student may need.

While you are in school, it is not a matter of if but when you will need help, so it is critical that you establish a robust list of resources that you can access anytime you are having trouble—one you can systematically move through until you find the answer you're looking for. Can't understand the material in the text? Check your lecture notes for any clarification. Notes aren't helping? Check your favorite websites and online resources. Can't find the answer online? Text or call your study group. Study group just as lost as you are? Email or call your TA and professor. Most importantly, never give up. Move through your list of resources until you find the answer. Remember, the pathway to your understanding *always* exists somewhere; you just need to find it.

You must understand that the pathway to your comprehension always exists. You just need to find it.

Part 2 — Application

It is one thing to have knowledge of something. It is quite another thing to be able to apply that knowledge. Your ability to successfully apply your knowledge will ultimately be what earns you a degree and a paycheck, for that matter. Having a solid understanding of material without the ability to apply it is like buying a brand-new car with no wheels—a lot of potential but essentially useless. Every exam you take will be testing your ability to apply what you've learned. By demonstrating that you can apply your knowledge to practical real-world situations, you are proving your understating of the material, and therefore your usefulness as an engineer. Once you graduate, your value as an engineer will be directly proportional to your ability to apply what you know to the real world. It is vital that you develop rock-solid application skills. In this section, we will go over how to do just that.

But before we delve into application, I want to reiterate the necessity of comprehension as a prerequisite to application. More comprehension feeds better application. This cannot be overstated. Comprehension is step one for a reason. It must come first. Oftentimes, students are tricked into thinking they can apply material because they've memorized a few ways to solve problems. Don't fall into this trap. Remember the tree analogy from earlier in this chapter? Don't get stranded out on those branches. This behavior is essentially gambling on your future. By first learning the core theory and principles, you will set yourself up for developing truly complete application competence. Comprehension comes first. Application comes second.

Observation

Before we attempt anything new on our own, it is always a good idea to observe someone who is experienced. For example, when you're first learning to ride a bike, a lot of information can be gained by watching others before you even make your first attempt: where to place your feet, how to hold the handlebars, which direction to pedal, how to brake, and how to steer and balance. All of this information can be obtained just by observing someone else apply their skill. By observing the proper application of knowledge, you are able to get an idea of what it will take for you to apply that same knowledge. The same can be said for studying. Whenever you are learning how to apply newly understood material, a great place to start is to observe numerous examples of that material being applied.

Textbook Examples: Textbooks are usually organized in such a way where they present and define a topic, then show some simple examples of that topic being applied. Don't ever skip over these examples! They are a perfect starting point for you to observe the proper application of the topic material.

Lecture Notes: Typically, when your professors are presenting new material, they will perform one or two example problems in front of the class. Pay attention! Make sure you understand how they were performed. Then copy the problems in your notes for later reference.

- -

PRO TIP: Always Document Lecture Examples. Keep in mind that professors usually select the problems that they perform in front of the class for a reason. There is a good chance that the types of problems they perform in front of the class will show up on the next exam. Be sure to always document these examples and make extra sure that you can perform the same type of problems come exam time.

- -

Online Examples: When you're looking for good examples, the internet is always a great source. Depending on the topic, you can usually find dozens of videos and written examples for anything and everything online. You can usually find several videos of other professors performing examples on YouTube. Also, Khan Academy is always great.

Homework

Once you have observed several examples of proper application and you are confident in your understanding, it's time for you to bust out that pencil and give it go. Fortunately for you, your professor will most likely assign some homework with exactly the type of problems you're looking to solve. This makes homework a great place to start as you're learning to apply what you've learned. Sometimes your professor will assign problems straight out of your textbook, and other times he or she will assign problems of his or her own creation. In either case, homework assignments will almost always have a nice mix of problems varying in difficulty, beginning with simpler problems that will test your basic understanding of the material and ending with more complicated problems that will comprehensively evaluate your abilities. It's usually a good bet that if you can complete your homework assignments unassisted, then you will be well prepared when tested on that material.

Solution Usage: While we're on the subject of homework, I think it is important to touch on one of the most powerful and potentially most harmful tools you can use while doing homework—solutions. Having fully worked-out solutions to your homework problems can really help in the verification of your own work. They can help guide you when you get stuck and can be very useful when you're studying for exams. However, having solutions available can be a little too tempting for many students (reference the previous section on Chegg). It can be very easy to look at a solution and say to yourself, "I totally understand this, and that is exactly how I would have solved it!" Don't fool yourself. Recognizing how a problem is solved is *very* different from solving it on your own unassisted. That is why having solutions is a major exercise in self-control and honesty. Be honest with yourself and make sure that you are using solutions as they were intended: to verify and guide your own work, not to replace it.

Practice, Practice, Practice: As the old saying goes, practice makes perfect. This is so true, especially when it comes to learning a new engineering application. By working through problems, you are essentially proving and enhancing your understanding of a topic. Whenever you're learning how to apply some new piece of knowledge, look for as many different problems as you can. Each problem will test your understanding from a new angle. This exercise will expose any holes in your understanding that need to be filled by further study. It is better to have these gaps exposed now as opposed to when you're taking an exam.

With continued practice, you will gain valuable experience that you can draw from in the future. You will develop an intuition that will guide you through future problems. Seek out every problem you can find: textbook problems, homework problems, online problems, and previous exam problems. Become a problem-solving machine. Make mistakes and learn from them. Then make more mistakes. Make all your mistakes during study time when they can't hurt you, rather than making them on an exam when they can hurt you. The more you practice, the better you will perform when it counts.

Presentation, Format, and Syntax: When learning how to apply material, you must always remember that you will not be the only person viewing your work. Your peers, TAs, and professors will all be learning from or grading your work at some point, so it's important that you learn how to present your work in an easy-to-understand manner. This means using the proper format, syntax, and presentation. Make sure your work is easy to follow and well organized. You should want your homework to be a stand-alone document, one that you can reference and study from easily. Below are a few tips and an example to make sure your homework is easy to understand and well organized.

⇒ Use yellow gridded engineering paper. It will help keep your work orderly and neat.

⇒ Don't worry about conserving space on your paper. Spread your work out for easier reading and grading.

⇒ Copy or summarize the problem statement at the top of the page.

⇒ List all relevant assumptions, variables, and equations at the top of each problem.

⇒ Draw any relevant diagrams or graphs.

⇒ Organize your work from top to bottom and left to right. This is how every textbook does it, so you should too.

⇒ Box your final answer and underline any preliminary answers.

⇒ Use an easy-to-erase pencil.

⇒ *Show all your work.* Make sure to copy down every step in solving any problem.

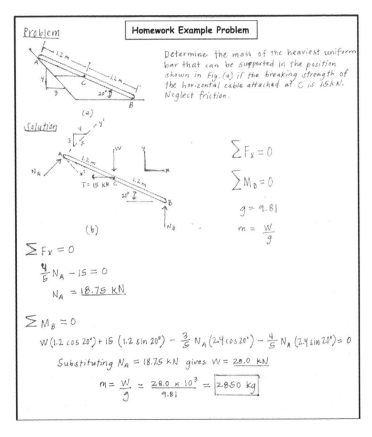

Remember that whatever you put down on paper will represent your knowledge. Whether it be a homework assignment, lab report, or a final exam. You may be a total master of a subject. You may understand every in and out of how to solve a problem. But it won't matter unless you can properly represent that knowledge on paper using a clear and organized format and presentation.

- -

PRO TIP: My Recommended Gear. Having quality gear is important. It needs to be reliable and robust. Below is the collection of my recommended gear for all your studying and exam-taking needs.

Pencil: Pentel Twist Erase Mechanical Pencil. This is the *best pencil ever.* This pencil is the ninth wonder of the world. Just buy one now. (Cost: 2 pack ~ $7)

Calculator: TI-89 Titanium. I love this calculator. It has every capability I needed and more, including calculus functionality, matrices, and a robust solver. Texas Instruments makes several equally capable calculators as well, like the TI-Nspire and the TI-84 series. (Cost ~ $100)

Notebook: Five Star Five Subject. These notebooks are ideal for note-taking and storing physical documents. They are robustly built and have perforated pages for clean page removal when needed. (Cost ~ $7)

Engineering Paper: TOPS Engineering Computation Pad. This is the paper that your professors will request for homework and other assignments. (Cost ~ $6)

Computer: MacBook Pro. I realize that this recommendation may have a large portion of you angry with me. But I'll have you know that I am currently writing this on an eleven-year-old MacBook Pro that is still working perfectly. Say what you want about operating systems and customization capabilities, when it comes to quality and robust hardware, nobody comes close to Apple. (Cost ~ $1300)

Part 3 — Retention

Once you have demonstrated sufficient comprehension and application of some material, the third and final step is retention. To make your knowledge truly useful, you must ensure it is sufficiently retained. Learning new material without successfully retaining it is like putting fuel into a car with no fuel tank. You need to retain what you've studied in order for your learning to become valuable. Your exam scores will depend on it. And although your brain is not as simple as a vehicle's fuel tank, there are several straightforward techniques to increase your brain's retention power. We have already gone over some of the most powerful in the previous chapter with the implementation of spaced repetition and taking breaks. I will not repeat them here. However, there are several other very powerful retention techniques that can be used in conjunction with spaced repetition and taking breaks to truly boost your ability to retain the material you've worked so hard to understand.

Test Yourself Constantly

We have already gone over the difference between recognition and recollection and how it can be very easy to look over material that you recognize and mistake that for recollection. A good way to prove that you can actually recall material is to consistently test yourself as you study. Don't wait until exam time to determine what you've retained. Test yourself as you go. Once you think you have grasped a concept, prove it to yourself by working out some problems without the help of solutions or notes. If you get hung up, figure out why right then and there. Then test yourself again and again until you are confident in your understanding and retention.

Teach Others

Once you're confident in your understanding of a given concept, try to teach it to one of your peers. Not only will you be helping another student in need, but you will also be testing your own understanding while developing greater retention of that concept. When teaching the material, try to perform the following five steps.

1. Summarize the material.
2. State the material into your own words.
3. Define relevant terms.
4. Present and explain real-world examples.
5. Answer any questions.

If there is anything that will poke holes in your own understanding, it's those five steps. I absolutely love this technique because it serves as such a great test of your own comprehension and retention. If you don't have any peers available, then teach a family member, a friend, or your dog! Just breaking the material down into simple terms and verbalizing it will go a long way in helping you to retain it.

Mnemonics

A mnemonic is a word, saying, rhyme, or image structured in a specific way to encode information, making it easier to retain. In order for a mnemonic to be effective, it must be much easier to remember than the information that it is encoding. A simple example would be the word HOMES as a way to remember the five great lakes: Huron, Ontario, Michigan, Erie, and Superior. When creating your own mnemonics, don't be afraid to get weird with it. Our brains tend to remember weird or funny things much better. So get your freak on. Below are some examples of the different types of mnemonics and how they can be used to aid you in retaining material.

Acronyms: *SOHCAHTOA* represents the three trigonometric functions used to define a right triangle (SinΘ = Opposite/Hypotenuse, CosΘ = Adjacent/Hypotenuse, TanΘ = Opposite/Adjacent). That is quite a lot of information packed into one word, which shows the power of a good acronym.

Sayings: *Please excuse my dear aunt sally* represents the order of operations in solving a math problem (Parentheses, Exponents, Multiplication, Division, Addition, Subtraction).

Rhymes: *Righty tighty, lefty loosey* represents the directions to turn threaded hardware for installation or removal.

Images: *Alligator eats the bigger number* is the imagery used to remember the definitions of the greater-than and less-than symbols in mathematics.

Chunking

Current science tells us that the average human brain has four slots in its working memory.[25] In other words, we can only hold four items in our mental focus at any one time. This seems pretty limited, doesn't it? If we are capped at four items, how can we improve on our retention capabilities? The trick is in the items themselves. When you think of four items, what do you imagine? Maybe you think of a banana, a tree, a coffee mug, and the letter *A*. That's pretty simple stuff, champ. But what if instead of your list from Sesame Street, the four

---

[25] Cowan, Nelson. "The Magical Mystery Four: How Is Working Memory Capacity Limited, and Why?" *Current Directions in Psychological Science* 19, no. 1 (February 2010): 51–57.

items were calculus, string theory, quantum mechanics, and the general theory of relativity? Whoa! Now we're talking. This is where the power of chunking comes in. With chunking, we can hack our own mental capability by forming meaningful connections between relatable material. These connections then grow and spread, forming a large chunk. This chunk can then be used in conjunction with other chunks to produce a much larger understanding of a subject.

Let me demonstrate with a simple example. In your mind, try to imagine the following four items at once: a tomato, a potato, an egg, and a tortilla. All four items are separate and unrelated. Do you have them all floating in your mind? Now, what if we were able to chunk these items together into one item? This would make it much easier to hold and add additional items to your working memory. To accomplish this, all you need to do is introduce some shared meaning. In this case, a simple breakfast burrito will do the trick. All four of these items combine to form the shared definition of a breakfast burrito. Now with this shared meaning, your mind creates connections between each item. These connections form a chunk. The newly formed chunk just effectively compressed four items into one, which enhances retention of each individual item while also freeing up room for more items in working memory. This process could be compared to creating a zip file on a computer. Once the shared meaning is established, your mind decreases the amount of memory needed to store it.

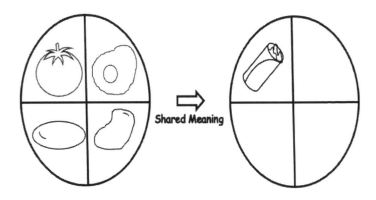

The breakfast burrito example above is simple, but it perfectly illustrates how, by introducing meaning, we can increase our retention capabilities. The more meaning that you can introduce, the more connections your mind will make and, in turn, use to create larger and larger chunks. I realize that we have entered into the realm of psychology and that this concept may be a bit obscure, but what it really boils down to is the importance of making connections between topics by developing a shared meaning between them.

Let's try another example by making a meaningful connection between physics and mathematics. In calculus, you will learn that the derivative of $(2x + 2) = 2$, which is not very exciting or memorable on its own. Now let's introduce some meaning with physics. Let's say that the function $2x + 2$ represents the velocity of an airplane as a function of position (x). So, at $x = 1$, we solve the equation and get a velocity of 4. And at $x = 0$ we get a velocity of 2, and so on. In physics, you will learn that the derivative of a velocity function will give you an object's acceleration. In this case, the acceleration is a constant two. Pretty cool, right? This application is much more interesting. We just took two chunks of separate information and combined them into one by applying them to each other. This ties in perfectly with the importance of making material

160

meaningful, which was discussed at the beginning of this chapter. By introducing a shared meaning, you are increasing your mind's ability to retain material and understand new material. If you want to know more about chunking, I recommend checking out Professor Barbara Oakley's TED talk and lectures on YouTube.[26]

The Importance of Sleep

There are few things that are more crucial to your ability to retain information than regular uninterrupted sleep. Trying to perform without it is like trying to run on ice. Sleep is a key ingredient in the process of converting new information into long-term memory. Current research shows that while we are awake and engaged, our brains create a ton of waste.[27] This waste is in the form of toxins known as metabolites. The longer we go without sufficient sleep, the more these toxins accumulate. Eventually, they build up to a point where they begin to literally interfere with the brain's ability to concentrate. Sleep to the rescue! A good night's sleep is the body's mechanism for literally flushing these toxins out of the brain, clearing the way for sharper focus and new memories to be solidified. It is important to note that this process cannot be replaced by caffeine or an energy drink. Sleep is the only way to truly recharge and cleanse your brain.

However, not all sleep is created equal. Three two-hour sessions do not equal one six-hour session. Your brain must be allowed to go through the proper cycles of sleep, especially

---

[26] Oakley, Barabara, "Learning How to Learn." Last modified August 5, 2014. Video, 17:50. https://www.youtube.com/watch?v=O96fE1E-rf8&t

[27] Fultz, Nina E., Giorgio Bonmassar, Kawin Setsompop, Robert A. Stickgold, Bruce R. Rosen, Jonathan R. Polimeni, and Laura D. Lewis. "Coupled Electrophysiological, Hemodynamic, and Cerebrospinal Fluid Oscillations in Human Sleep." *Science* 366, no. 6465 (November 2019): 628–631.

the deepest cycle where your brain waves are at their slowest, also known as REM sleep. The current scientific consensus suggests that this stage is the most important for memory consolidation.[28] While a quick nap here and there can be very helpful, naps cannot replace your regular nightly sleep session. Do not make the mistake of thinking you can sacrifice sleep to make room for longer study sessions or some late-night partying. The occasional late night before an exam will be unavoidable. Just don't make a habit of it.

Most healthy adults need between seven and nine hours of sleep to function at their mental best. I personally need between seven and eight hours each night, or else I feel like my brain is trying to think through a thick layer of sludge. If you've ever gone several days in a row on less than five hours of sleep, you know what I'm talking about. You quickly transform into a much less effective version of yourself. Don't let this happen. At this point in your life, you should know how much sleep you need to function normally. You may be able to shave off fifteen or thirty minutes here and there, but be careful. I would not recommend going too far below seven hours. The consequences are just not worth it. Protect your sleep at all costs. Remember that sustainability is the key to success.

The Power of Exercise

The science is clear. When it comes to staying healthy, regular exercise is the single most beneficial habit that any human can develop (which is why I keep bringing it up). Below is a short list of just some of the major benefits of regular exercise.[29]

---

[28] Stickgold, R. "Sleep-Dependent Memory consolidation." *Nature* 437 (2005): 1272–1278.

[29] Gomez-Pinilla, Fernando and Charles Hillman. "The Influence of Exercise on Cognitive Abilities." *Comprehensive Physiology* 3, no. 1 (January 2013): 403–428.

⇒ Reduces the risk of chronic diseases like cancer, cardio-vascular disease, and diabetes
⇒ Reduces stress
⇒ Increases energy
⇒ Boosts mood
⇒ Improves sleep
⇒ Decreases depression and anxiety
⇒ Strengthens bones and muscles
⇒ Promotes happiness
⇒ Increases confidence

I think it's safe to say that most of the medicine cabinets in this country wouldn't be so full if everyone developed a habit of regular exercise. I could write several chapters on the benefits listed above. But because this book is about succeeding in engineering school, I will try to focus on the direct impact exercise has as it relates to your performance in school.

Improved Memory and Creativity: Regular aerobic exercise (the kind where your heart rate is elevated for thirty minutes) directly promotes the growth and survival of brain cells in the hippocampus, the part of the brain responsible for memory, high-level thinking, and creativity.

Improved Focus: Studies show that just one session of intense aerobic exercise can immediately boost the performance of the prefrontal cortex,[30] the part of the brain responsible for focus and decision-making. It's like a boost of cranial power. Think of the Fast & Furious movies. Nitro!

---

[30] Moriarty, Terence, Kelsey Bourbeau, Bryanne Bellovary, and Micah N. Zuhl. "Exercise Intensity Influences Prefrontal Cortex Oxygenation during Cognitive Testing." *Behavioral Sciences* 9, no. 8 (July 2019).

Increases Performance and Waste Management: Blood is the brain's fuel source. Without a constant flow of blood, your brain's performance will suffer greatly. Blood carries oxygen and nutrients through the body while also carrying away carbon dioxide and other waste. By increasing your heart rate, you will increase blood flow to your brain, therefore increasing performance and waste disposal.

Long-Term Mental Health: Not surprisingly, regular aerobic exercise is also one of the most effective ways you can ensure long-term mental health. There is mounting evidence showing that regular exercise decreases the likelihood of depression, anxiety, and dementia.[31]

Many people overcomplicate exercise to the point where it is more of a chore than it needs to be. In reality it's super simple. You don't need any special equipment, expensive gym passes, or all the latest gear. All you need is fifteen to thirty minutes a day and a good pair of shoes. It can be as simple as doing some good old-fashioned push-ups and sit-ups in your bedroom or, even better, going for a jog or a bike ride outside. Speaking of outside, I recommend exercising outside as much as possible. Get as close to nature as you can. Mountain biking and trail running are some of my personal favorites for this reason. There is an added stress reduction benefit to getting outside under the sun and into the fresh air, even if it's just your neighborhood park.[32] Figure out what is sustainable for

---

[31] Ashish Sharma, MD, Vishal Madaan, MD, and Frederick D. Petty, MD, PhD. "Exercise for Mental Health." *Primary Care Companion Journal of Clinical Psychiatry* 8, no. 2 (2006): 106.

[32] Coon, J. Thompson, K. Boddy, K. Stein, R. Whear, J. Barton, M. H. Depledge. "Does Participating in Physical Activity in Outdoor Natural Environments Have a Greater Effect on Physical and Mental Well-Being than Physical Activity Indoors? A Systematic Review." *Environmental Science and Technology* 45, no. 5 (2011):1761–1772.

you and build a habit. Your stress levels and overall mental performance will thank you.

I realize that time is going to be your most valuable commodity during school. Because of this, exercise will most likely be one of the activities that gets neglected. But hopefully some of what was just discussed will change your mind. The mental benefits offered by regular aerobic exercise are undeniable. I personally feel these benefits every day—better mood, lower stress, sharper mind, more energy, better memory, and more creativity to name a few. Trust me, your return on investment will be tenfold. Just think of it as routine mental maintenance, your regular mental oil change, if you will—not optional. As you create your schedule each semester, make sure to leave room for a regular exercise routine. Even fifteen to twenty minutes a day will do. Your health and sanity will thank you.

Quick Recap

Your ability to study effectively and consistently is the most important skill you will cultivate as a student. You will be paving the road to your degree by developing it. For a study session to be truly effective, it must include three essential ingredients: comprehension, application, and retention. Let's go through a quick recap of each.

Comprehension is the first step to learning anything, and it begins with your textbook. *Read every damn page.* Utilize tools like SQ3R to get the most out of your reading. Make material meaningful by connecting it to material that you already know. When you don't understand something, remember that you're not alone. Take advantage of all your lifelines: professors, TAs, peers, and online resources. Never let any question go unanswered. Your comprehension is the foundation that everything is built upon.

Once you feel confident in your comprehension, the next step is to apply what you know. Your ability to apply knowledge will be what earns you a degree and ultimately a paycheck. Utilize your homework, textbook examples, and online resources to sharpen your application skills. Search for any holes in your understanding by solving every problem you can find. You must fill these holes now before they are exposed on an exam.

The last step in a successful study session is retention. You must be able to retain and reproduce what you've learned in order for it to be of any value in the future. As you study, test yourself consistently, and try to teach what you know to your peers. Utilize the power of chunking by making meaningful connections between material. And last but not least, never ever neglect sleep or exercise. When it comes to your ability to concentrate and retain information, there is simply no substitute for either. Make sleep and exercise a priority.

Becoming an effective studier is simply a requirement for success in engineering school. By implementing the tools and techniques discussed in the last two chapters, you will be arming yourself with the habits that will carry you through to graduation and beyond.

NINE

EXAMS

An ounce of performance is worth pounds of promises.
—Mae West

The Importance of Exams

Depending on your particular curriculum, your degree will require around 120 credits, which equates to roughly 40 separate courses. Assuming that each course has at least two midterms and one final exam, you're facing approximately 120 exams total. Overall, these exams will account for roughly 50 percent to 70 percent of your final grade in each course. This means that just one ninety-minute exam could account for over 20 percent of your overall grade in a given course. That is the difference between an A and a C. Are your palms getting sweaty yet? I am not trying to scare you. But you must understand how critical it is to do well on your exams. Your performance on homework, labs, and projects is important, but when we're talking about your final grade, exams are *the* difference

167

maker. Your homework, labs, and projects exist to help you develop your knowledge and skills. Exams are the place where you must demonstrate that knowledge and skill. If you're unable to do so, you will not pass the course, plain and simple.

That is why I've dedicated an entire chapter to exam performance. It is just too important to not address comprehensively. I've broken the subject down into three sections. Each section will explore what you should be doing before, during, and after an exam. Do your best to absorb and implement the information in this chapter because your exam performance should not be taken lightly. The feeling you get after performing poorly on an exam is not something that is easily overcome. It can drain your motivation and breed self-doubt. I don't want you to ever feel that way. Take this chapter seriously, and you will become well-armed in the high-stakes world of exams.

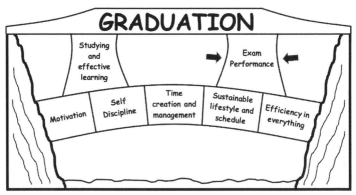

The Bridge of Graduation

Before an Exam

First, I want to emphasize what you should already know but maybe don't want to admit to yourself. The *only* way to consistently guarantee high performance on exams is to study appropriately. I hate to break it to you, but there is no magic technique that will transform an exam score from 50 percent to 95 percent. Proper preparation is the only safe bet. Yes, you may get lucky from time to time, and your professor may throw some softballs. But why risk it? When so much of your success depends on just a few exams per course, they should be approached with maximum effort every time. Think about it this way. Will you ever regret overpreparing for an A? Probably not. But I can guarantee you that you will regret underpreparing for an F. There is just no substitute for proper preparation.

In almost every case I have encountered, when a student complains about a low test score, their preparation and study habits were to blame. Although they may initially blame unfair test questions, professor biases, inadequate time, or test anxiety, in almost all cases, the real culprit is inadequate preparation. I am not denying that unfair test questions, professor biases, inadequate time, and test anxiety exist, because they do. However, they should only be considered after you're 100 percent confident in your own preparation. And just to give you an idea, I personally did not reach this level of confidence until I had invested around twenty-five to thirty-five hours of quality study time before an exam. This investment may be different for you. But the important thing is that you be honest with yourself when trying to determine a cause for any less-than-ideal exam score. More often than not, the reason for poor performance is insufficient preparation. Always start there. Only when you can honestly tell yourself that you were well prepared can you assign the blame elsewhere. With that, let's dive into proper exam preparation.

Will you ever regret overpreparing for an A? Probably not. But I can guarantee that you will regret underpreparing for an F.

Schedule Your Study Time: The obvious first step in exam prep is to actually give yourself enough time to study (reference chapter 5). For me, that meant blocking out two or three full days prior to each exam. The best way to accomplish this is to schedule these study days at the beginning of the semester before your calendar fills up. On the first day of class, every professor should hand out a course schedule containing the date of every exam throughout the semester. You can use these dates to schedule your study days. Add the dates to your personal schedule and set reminders in your phone. If you work, you should request these days off. Also, you should plan for more time than you think you'll need. That way, you'll have the time if you end up needing it. The last thing you want is to be strapped for time if the material is tougher than expected. It's always better to be safe than sorry. Schedule the time early and do not let anything else take precedence. Your exam study time has the largest potential impact on your grade, so it should be considered sacred and nonnegotiable.

My Study Plan: At the beginning of chapter 4, I told you about the summer of my sophomore year, when I completely overhauled my study habits. As a part of that effort, I totally rebuilt my exam preparation process. I largely credit this change for my success thereafter. That three- to four-day process was as follows:

⇒ **Day 1 (10–12 hours):** Thoroughly read or reread the relevant chapters in the textbook. Absorb all examples and topics. Email or meet with professor, TA, or peers to get all questions answered that arose from the reading.

⇒ **Day 2 (10–12 hours):** Finish any reading. Rework through all corresponding homework and previous exams (if provided). Work through the study guide (if provided). Begin to create an equation sheet (if relevant). Email or meet with the professor, TA, or peers to get any questions answered that arose from studying.

⇒ **Day 3 (10–12 hours):** Finalize equation sheet (if relevant). Rerun through the work done on day two. Retake practice exams. Teach peers as needed. Email or meet with the professor, TA, or peers to get any remaining questions answered. Get a good night's sleep.

⇒ **Day 4 – exam day (0.5–1 hour):** On exam day refresh from your equation sheet and previously worked problems to get the gears moving prior to the exam. Avoid trying to learn new material on exam day. In my experience, this tends to compromise what you already know. Eat a nutritious breakfast and do a quick workout if possible.

If you've implemented the topics that have been presented in the previous chapters and are studying regularly throughout the semester, you probably won't need to study this intensely for each exam. Ideally, your exam study sessions should be just a review of what you've already learned up to that point. Nevertheless, with the heavy weight that exams have on your grades, an intense study plan is a good place to start. The above study plan increased my average exam score by two full letter grades, going from the C-/C range to the B+/A− range.

It worked for me, and it will likely for you too. If you're struggling with exams, I'd give it a try. Then, as your experience increases, you can iterate the process to make your own. What's most important is that you find what works for you and stick with it.

Regardless of your exact process for exam prep, there are a few constants that should always be included when preparing for an exam.

Clarify What Will Be Covered: Get a firm handle on what the exam will and will not cover. Usually, your professors will provide these details. But if they don't, make sure you get the exam content clarified. You'll want all of your study time to be spent on material that you will *actually* be tested on.

Clarify the Type of Exam: There is a big difference between studying for a fifty-question multiple-choice exam and studying for a three-question problem-solving exam. Before you begin your preparation, make sure to clarify this with your professors. By knowing how you will be tested, you can adjust your approach to best compliment the type of exam.

Know Your Professor's Style: Every professor has a different style when it comes to exams. Some like to ask questions that are simple and straightforward, and others will ask you to solve near-impossible problems. Some will ask questions similar to what is in the homework and textbook, and others will base questions on their lecture material. Some value the correct answer, and others value the correct approach. Some will curve the results, and others will not. Knowing these things about your professors is very valuable prior to taking any exam. Talk to upperclassmen and get your hands on previous exams if possible. Knowing your professor's style will help to guide your study approach.

Refresh the Underlying Material: Ideally, you should already have a good handle on the underlying material before an exam. But if you don't, it is the best place to start. Just memorizing the way a few problems were performed on the homework won't get you very far. Professors will test your understanding of the core material, so you should expect them to throw some curveballs that truly test your understanding on every exam.

Get All Questions Answered: Don't let *any* question go unanswered. During your studying, write down all questions that come up. Most will be answered as you continue to study. However, you must be sure to email or visit with your professor or TA to get all remaining questions answered. If you still have questions before an exam, you can only blame yourself if you perform poorly.

Test Yourself: The best way to determine if you're ready for an exam is to test yourself. There is a big difference between being able to follow an already-worked-out problem and being able to work one out on your own from scratch. Just because you understand something when looking at it doesn't mean you can do it on your own unassisted. Put yourself in the exam atmosphere before the actual exam and test yourself with new problems. This is the best way to determine your readiness level.

Get a Good Night's Sleep: We have already touched on the importance of sleep a few times in this book. But it's worth bringing up again. Adequate sleep is essential to performing at your highest level, so try not to sacrifice your sleep on the night prior to an exam. Your ability to think clearly and process complex material depends on it.

Exam Day Warm-Up: It is well known that before any physical competition, it's a good idea to stretch and warm up your muscles. Warming up increases blood flow and loosens up stiff joints, therefore helping to maximize your body's performance. The same can be said for your brain on exam day. You do not want to waste precious exam time waiting for your brain to wake up after the exam has already begun, so make sure it is adequately warmed up before the exam begins.

Wake up early and eat a good breakfast. Go for a walk or do a quick workout to increase blood flow. Go through a few problems that you already know how to do. And be sure to arrive early so you can prepare any and all materials before your professor hands anything out. These things will ensure that your brain is ready to rock the moment your professor says, "Begin."

Be Humble: If you are not getting the exam scores you want, then something is most likely wrong with your studying process. Be willing to admit this to yourself and scrap anything that isn't working. Always remember that the pathway to good test scores exists; you just need to find it. Keep iterating your process until you find what works, then stick to it.

During an Exam

When I think of taking an engineering exam, I think of the old Sega video game *Sonic the Hedgehog*. In the game, Sonic attempts to traverse the level as fast as possible while collecting as many rings as possible. Some areas have more rings than others, and some rings are harder to obtain than others. If you know what you're doing, you can adjust your play to gather more rings in a shorter amount of time. And if you're inexperienced, you may leave several easy rings uncollected. The same can be said for taking exams. Not all of the points are distributed evenly. Some questions will be worth more than others, and some points will take more time to earn than others. It is important that you adjust your approach accordingly. The good news is that there are many useful ways to strategize around this reality. Below is a list of the different steps and techniques you can utilize while taking an exam. They will help you to maximize the points you earn by managing your time more efficiently.

Survey: The first thing you should do when your professor hands you an exam (after you put your name on it, of course) is to do a quick survey of the questions and their point values. This quick scan should give you an approximate idea of how much time you should be spending on each question. For example, a sixty-minute exam is worth one hundred points with five questions at ten, ten, twenty, twenty, and forty point values. Your time spent on each problem should look something like six minutes, six minutes, twelve minutes, twelve minutes, and twenty-four minutes, respectively. If you've spent twenty minutes on a ten-point question, that's probably too long, especially since the last question is worth forty points. So, before you begin, take note of any large-point-valued questions. Your time spent on each question should be proportional to their point values. A quick survey before you begin will give you this knowledge.

Cut Your Losses: When it comes down to it, if you're not actively answering questions, then you're not earning points. If you get stuck on a problem or a question for too long, it may be time to cut your losses and move on. Keep the big picture in mind. Yes, if you spent all of the remaining time, then you may be able to solve that one problem. But you will probably leave more points on the table by neglecting any other unanswered questions. And oftentimes, the answer you were looking for may hit you like a ton of bricks once you have moved on. I can't tell you how many times this happened to me while taking an exam, so don't hesitate to move on if you're stuck on a question. Answer the questions you know first and bank those points. Then if you have time, go back and work on any speed bumps.

Make Assumptions: Many of your exams will include problems that require a large number of steps to complete. What do you do if you get stuck on step four of a twenty-step problem? You make an educated assumption and move on. If you know how to perform the remaining sixteen steps, you shouldn't let one speed bump stop you in your tracks. Most professors care more about your knowledge of the overall method rather than the accuracy of your answers. If you slip up on one step, chances are good that your professor will be forgiving if you worked out the rest of the problem correctly. Yes, your final answer might be incorrect, but how you got there will be mostly correct and your score should reflect that. If you get stuck on a step for too long, make an educated assumption, then state that assumption on your exam and move on. This technique saved me a ton of points on multiple exams throughout my degree.

Slow Down and Read Carefully: If you're going to spend twenty to thirty minutes working out one problem, you better make sure that your work matches up with the problem statement. In the atmosphere of an exam, it is very easy to rush through reading a problem statement. This can lead you down the wrong road as you work out the problem. So slow down and read each question multiple times before you put pencil to paper. If you think a problem is underconstrained or becoming way too complicated, it's probably because you missed something in the problem statement.

Use All of the Allotted Time: Taking an engineering exam is almost always a battle against time. In many cases, I would feel content if I was just able to answer all of the questions within the allotted time. But, if you do happen to finish your exam early, make good use of the extra time and verify any questionable answers that you may have had, focusing on the high-point-value problems first. Be smart and utilize all of the time you are given. You may find a couple of extra points that you left on the table.

Managing Distractions: Nothing is worse than being yanked out of the zone by some sick student coughing or sniffing every eight seconds. You didn't study for the last three days straight just to be thwarted by Snotty Sam. Pack some ear-plugs or noise-canceling headphones (if your professor will allow it). Also, arrive early and spread out. Take up as much space as possible. This will decrease the chances of some distracting student sitting right next to you. Lastly, never be afraid to speak up or move to another location in the classroom if you feel too distracted. Your exam time is too important.

PRO TIP: Carry Extra Batteries and Lead. Always, always, always bring extra batteries, lead, paper, and erasers to every exam. Losing precious time because your calculator died or because you ran out of supplies is unacceptable.

Test Anxiety

Feeling a little nervous or anxious before an exam is totally appropriate. However, for those with test anxiety, a simple exam could cause debilitating thoughts of failure, lack of focus, headaches, and even nausea. Current research from the American Test Anxiety Association suggests that around 20 percent of students suffer from some level of test anxiety. Most students are able to manage their anxiety without letting it affect their performance too much. But for others, it can be severely debilitating. Wherever you may be on this spectrum, the advice for preventing and managing test anxiety is pretty much the same.

Do Well Early: One of the most common causes of test anxiety is a previous experience with poor performance. The experience was so terrible that the student's mind developed the anxiety response as a defense mechanism. Then the fear becomes so distracting that they ended up doing poorly on the next exam, therefore creating another bad experience—and so the cycle begins. The best way to prevent this cycle from forming is to replace that first poor experience with a good one. Then a similar cycle will begin, fed by good experiences instead of bad, breeding confidence instead of fear.

Even if you don't have an issue with test anxiety, doing well on the first exam of a given course is crucial. I cannot overstate this. Your first exam sets the tone for the rest of the semester. If you do poorly, it can feel like you just took three steps backward. Then to make up for the bad score, you have to kick it into overdrive for the rest of the semester. Conversely, if you do well on the first exam, your confidence will be supercharged. The remainder of the semester won't be as daunting because you've already proven to yourself that you can succeed. Do everything you can to knock your first exams out of the park. Then as you begin to perform well, it will become easier and easier to keep performing well. Momentum is very real and very powerful, so you should utilize it.

Stop Empowering the Anxiety: There are two types of anxiety. The first type is based on a real threat, like being chased by a bear. And the second type is based on no real threat, like being afraid of an exam. For those with severe test anxiety, their brain reacts the same to an exam as it would to a pursuing bear—extreme fear and discomfort. They go into fight or flight mode. This is a totally inappropriate and disproportionate response. The exam will not kill you, the world will not end, you will not be kicked out of school, and you're actually pretty smart! By acknowledging the inappropriate anxiety and allowing it to influence your behavior, you're validating it. And when you validate it, your mind will think it's reacting the correct way and it will continue to do so. The way to stop this reaction is to no longer acknowledge the anxiety. Then over time your brain will be rewired to stop reacting inappropriately.

In order to retrain an anxious mind, you will need to be able to quickly distinguish between a normal thought or feeling and an anxious thought or feeling. If the thought or feeling is an anxious one, you must immediately discard it like a piece of smelly garbage and quickly move all of your focus to something productive. Do not let it take hold of you. Because before you know it, you will be on that downward spiral of self-doubt and fear, and you know that's not going to get you anywhere. As you get better at recognizing the anxiety early and quickly diverting your attention elsewhere, your mind will begin to reprogram its response back to a nonanxious one.

It is important to note that I am not a doctor or a professional therapist. However, I do have personal experience with severe anxiety. I know firsthand how completely debilitating it can be. Fortunately, I was able to eliminate my anxiety using a method very similar to the one described above. It is called The Linden Method (www.thelindenmethod.co.uk), and if you're suffering from any anxiety-related conditions, I highly recommend it.

After an Exam

Your exam is over. Woohoo! Time to party! Whoa, whoa, whoa—not so fast. There are still a few things you should know and do before you turn into a vegetable and take residence on the couch. Opportunities still exist even after an exam is over. And depending on how you performed, you may be feeling like a million bucks, like some fresh roadkill, or somewhere in between. Dealing with these emotions quickly and productively is a very important skill that you'll need to develop. There is always another exam approaching on the horizon, so the faster you can learn from your mistakes and get your mind back to ground level, the better.

Verify Your Score: Once your professor returns your graded exam, the first thing you should do is thoroughly comb through the scoring of every problem. Make sure you agree with your professor's reasoning for any docked points. If you don't agree, or if you notice any scoring mistakes, meet with him or her immediately. No professor is perfect. They make mistakes just like the rest of us. Most are reasonable and will give you back a couple of points here and there, so take advantage of this. Exam points are precious; never ever leave any on the table.

Once your score is finalized, it's time to fill the gaps in your knowledge and learn from your mistakes, especially while the exam material is still fresh. If you're lucky, your professor will go over every exam problem in detail during the next lecture, clearing up any confusion you may have had on the points you missed. However, if your professor does not take the time to do this, make sure you do. It's a good bet that this isn't the last time you will see that material on an exam, especially if the course has a comprehensive final exam. You should immediately set up a meeting with your professor or TA and take the time to fully understand all of your mistakes and the reasoning for any missed points. This will help prepare you for the next time you encounter the material.

Another great reason to meet with your professor after an exam is the potential for an exam retake. Not all professors offer this option, but if they do, it may be worth your while. I personally had a professor that would let us retake any exam problems that we missed points on. If we performed better, then he would give us half of a point back for every point we initially missed. This saved my grade a couple of times throughout that semester. Professors like to see a willingness to learn and improve. If you're meeting with them regularly and are consistently demonstrating hard work, they are sometimes willing to offer a retake option. Keep in mind that they won't always advertise these options, so make sure you ask. It never hurts to ask.

If You Did Well: Whether you scored 100 percent or 10 percent, the faster you can get your mind back to ground level, the better. The emotions that can come from a very high or very low score can do funny things to your productivity. For instance, if you do very well on an exam, it can sometimes feel like a ticket to slow down or decrease effort. Dwelling on a high score can sometimes produce a false sense of security. It can make you think that you don't have to work as hard for the next exam. Don't let this happen. The faster you can put it behind you, the better. It's okay to celebrate, but don't let it go to your head. Keep in mind that this was just one exam of many. Consistent high scores are what you really want, and the only way to achieve this is through consistent hard work and continuous improvement. Whether you scored 50 percent or 95 percent, always learn from your mistakes and move forward quickly.

If You Did Poorly: Now, what if your score is on the lower end of the spectrum? What if your score is so low that you're embarrassed to tell anyone? I've been there multiple times, so I know firsthand how these situations can be particularly difficult to recover from. A low score can really take a toll on your motivation and confidence. But your priorities should remain the same. Learn from your mistakes and move forward as quickly as possible. A low exam score hurts no matter who you are. But what is important is how you channel those emotions. You must make them work for you before they become toxic. When I would perform poorly, I would use my disappointment as motivation to change my study habits and work harder. Failure can be your greatest teacher if you let it. If and when you perform poorly on an exam, you should immediately begin the following process.

1. Meet with your professor to understand why you missed the points you missed.

2. Fill the gaps in your knowledge that caused you to miss those points.

3. Ask yourself how you could have prepared better in the first place to prevent those gaps in knowledge from forming and adjust your study process accordingly.

4. Ask yourself what changes you can implement now to prevent low scores in the future. Then immediately act on those changes.

5. Remind yourself that engineering school is just as much a test of your resiliency as it is of your intelligence. It is

very uncommon for any student to fly through school without a bad exam score here and there. Remind yourself that you're not alone and you're still where you belong.

Remember that a single exam score does not reflect your overall capability or potential. It only reflects how well you prepared for that one particular exam. That's it! Be resilient and don't let a bad score define you. Learn your lessons and move on quickly.

- -

A single exam score does not reflect your overall capability or potential. It only reflects how well you prepared for that one particular exam.

- -

Comparing Yourself to Others

At this point, I think it's important that I touch on the significance of comparing yourself to other students. Making comparisons, especially exam score comparisons, can either be a very powerful motivator or a very powerful demotivator. The key is to maintain perspective. You must realize that everyone in your class begins at a different level. Yes, you all begin as freshmen. But everyone's study habits and test taking skills will be vastly different. At one end of the spectrum, there will be the wiz-kids who seem to ace every exam without ever opening the textbook, and on the other end will be the students who seem to have absolutely no idea what they're doing. All of the students on this spectrum have the same potential. The difference is that the wiz-kids have already invested the necessary time and effort to strengthen their minds and build good study habits. Don't forget these facts when you make your own comparisons. If you're not getting the exam scores you want, that does not mean you are any less capable than anyone else. It only means that you need to invest more time and effort to strengthen your own mind and study habits.

On the other hand, if you're a highly competitive person like me, comparing your performance to others may be a very beneficial exercise. There's nothing like a little healthy competition to bring out the best in everyone. Obviously, you don't want to be comparing yourself to people failing every exam. That wouldn't get you very far. Your goal should be continuous improvement, so you'll want to consistently compare yourself to people who perform a little better than you on every exam. Then once you begin to consistently outperform those students, choose a new group to compare yourself to. Ideally, there will be some healthy competition within your own study group, where you all benefit continuously by pushing each other.

Maybe you're not the competitive type. Or maybe you get discouraged easily when you make comparisons to others. This is totally fine. You should only use competition with others if it helps you improve. However, there is one person who you should constantly compare yourself to. And that's the old you. Measuring your current performance against your own past performances is probably the most accurate and appropriate measurement for personal improvement that you can make. At the very least, be sure to make this comparison almost daily.

There is one person who you should constantly compare yourself to. And that's the old you.

Quick Recap

There is no way around it. In order to graduate, you must perform well on your exams. They carry more weight toward your final grades than anything else by far, so you must approach them with a proportional amount of focus and effort. Start by planning your study time at the beginning of the semester. Block out study days on your calendar and treat your study time as sacred and nonnegotiable. Formulate a study plan and keep adjusting it until you're getting the results you want.

When you are taking an exam, use the allotted time efficiently. Create a plan of attack based on a quick scan of every problem. And focus your efforts on large-point-valued problems. Once an exam is over and you have received your results, make sure you agree with the score. Quickly fill the gaps in your knowledge that caused any missed points, then move forward. Get your mind back to ground level as quickly as possible. Don't let a high score go to your head or a low score destroy you. And lastly, be mindful of the potential dangers and advantages of comparing your performance to others. If it helps, do it. If it doesn't help, don't do it. We would all love a world without exams. Unfortunately, their existence is necessary. But if you give them the attention they deserve from the beginning, you will be just fine.

TEN

PLANNING FOR YOUR CAREER

The moment you know what you want should be the same
moment you begin its pursuit.

The Big Picture

While you're in school, it will be easy to forget that it will end
in just a few short years. That's right, school will end, and you
will become a degreed engineer. At that point, you will make
the transition from being a full-time student to being a full-
time professional. For many students, this transition can leave
them feeling rather unprepared and a bit shocked. Over the
past four to five years, they've spent so much time worrying
about their performance in their classes that they may have
neglected the most important questions a student can ask
themselves.

What do I want to do with my degree?

Where do I want to work?

Where do I want to live?

What lifestyle do I want?

How much money does that lifestyle cost?

These five questions should shape your life after school is over. Don't make the mistake of waiting until graduation to ask them. In fact, they should be in the back of your mind starting day one of freshman year. Think about them regularly and let them guide you. Why? Because besides your coursework, there is a hell of a lot you can be doing while you're in school to land your dream career. This final chapter will help you lay the groundwork for finding and obtaining that career.

Don't Go Money Blind

The number of career pathways that engineering provides is substantial. Refer to chapter 2 for a list of just some of these career paths. In fact, you'd be hard pressed to find an industry that engineering isn't a part of in some capacity. There is no denying that the opportunity will be substantial. For this reason, it's important that you attempt to choose a career direction while you're still in school. The last thing you want is to graduate and just take the first job that offers you a decent paycheck. And trust me, this will be tempting, especially when you've been scraping by on a student's wage. Those dollar signs can be quite blinding.

It's important to take a step back and remember that you just worked your butt off to get your degree, so you owe it to yourself to leverage it to its absolute potential. Remind yourself that the unemployment rate for engineers is always much lower than the national average. According to the Bureau of Labor Statistics, 140,000 new engineering jobs will be created in the next ten years, so you shouldn't worry too much about finding a decent-paying job. They will most likely be a dime a dozen. Try to focus on what you'll actually be doing first, then worry about the pay. Your first job will set the tone for the rest of your career, so you shouldn't take its selection lightly.

Choosing Your Career Path

Whether it be mechanical, electrical, chemical, civil, software, or somewhere in between, your specific field of study has already narrowed your career path significantly. Now it's time to get even more specific. What type of work do you think you'd enjoy doing? Is that type of work available in your area? These are the types of questions you need to try to answer. And only then should you move on to step two, which is to begin aggressively pursuing your chosen career path. Don't worry if at this point you actually have no idea what career you want to pursue. Most young college students don't. I was one of them. However, you should begin to act toward answering these questions now. Below is a list of some things you can do now to help you determine your specific career direction.

Step Outside Your Comfort Zone

It can be very difficult to purposefully expose yourself to uncomfortable situations. However, I can tell you from personal experience that these are the situations that will teach you the most about yourself, so say yes to every potential opportunity even if it's a little scary or obscure. You could study abroad, accept an out-of-state internship, take some workplace tours, or just take some funky elective courses. Think about it this way: if you're unsure about what you want to do career-wise, then you're not going to gain any insight by remaining in the realm of the known. You must step outside into the realm of the unknown to learn some valuable things about what you want to do.

Do Research

This one is a bit obvious, but that doesn't make it any less important. If you have some interest in a potential career, then research it! Find out what those engineers actually do every day. And keep in mind that job roles change drastically from company to company. A process engineer at a chemical plant will have a very different job role than a process engineer at a manufacturing facility. Take some time to really learn the details of different careers. Then try to imagine yourself in those roles.

Meet Engineers

If you want to know more about any topic, where is the best place to go? The source, of course! Get a list together of every engineer you know. Ask your friends and family if they know any engineers and if they can provide their contact information. Then set up a meeting or phone call with every engineer on your list. Get to know them and find out what they do on a daily basis in detail. Most will be more than happy to talk with you. And not only will you learn a great deal from these conversations, but you will be adding some great contacts to your network (more on networking later). Additionally, most universities offer meet and greets with actual engineers throughout the year. Take advantage of these offerings. And lastly, ask every engineer that you speak with to provide some other engineering contacts who you can talk with. Every engineer usually has a large network of other engineers who may be able to assist in your quest for career knowledge.

Pursuing Your Career Path

Once you've really narrowed down your career path, it is time to begin aggressively pursuing that path. It's never too early to start your pursuit. Even if you've known exactly what you've wanted to do since you were four years old, it's still not too early. The moment you know what you want should be the same moment you start your pursuit. Now you may be asking, "How do I pursue my career before I graduate?" I have two words for you: networking and internships. Besides actually obtaining your degree, these two things will take you farther toward landing your dream career than anything else. In the following pages, we will explore each one individually and show how they can be utilized to get you where you want to be.

Networking

You've likely heard the phrase "It's not what you know but who you know." Maybe you never gave it much thought. Maybe you brushed it off as just something people say. Well, that stops now. That phrase contains way more truth than you may think. The value of collecting a good network of people cannot be overstated. We live in a world full of people, and your connections with those people can lift you into places that would have been unachievable on your own.

Your network consists of absolutely everyone you know: family, friends, coworkers, neighbors, classmates...everyone. Take a moment to think about your own network. Who do you know? Do you currently know anyone who may be able to help you in your career quest? How healthy are those relationships? Who could help you that you haven't met yet? How can you add them to your network? These are the questions you should be asking because it is undeniable that a strong network is one of the most powerful assets for any professional. Below you will find the three ingredients to creating a strong network.

Step 1: Meet People. Creating a solid network is a numbers game. The more people you meet, the higher your chances are of meeting someone who may be valuable to you, so get out there! There are opportunities to meet people everywhere— school, work, gym, park, grocery store. I'm not telling you to stop every person you see and force them into a conversation. That would be weird. This is more about putting yourself in the right situations and then taking advantage of opportunities when they arise. For example, I literally got my first internship interview through a guy I randomly met playing pickup racquetball. Don't call it luck. I increased my odds for opportunity, and I eventually cashed in. It's just a numbers game. Trust me, this stuff works.

The key is exposing yourself to new groups of people— the more the better. You may be a little shy or introverted. But let me tell you that developing some good interpersonal skills is one of the most valuable things an engineer can do. It really can differentiate you from the rest of the field when it comes time to start interviewing for jobs. Most companies will fight over an engineer who is both technically savvy and a good communicator, so you should look at this as an opportunity to grow both your network and your interpersonal skills.

Step 2: Develop the Relationship. Once you've made some good contacts, it's time to develop and nurture those relationships. The first and most important step here is to be genuine. Real, long-lasting relationships are built on trust. The people you meet should be able to trust that you're actually being yourself. Don't put on a mask or adopt some alternate personality that you think will win people over. If you want real, enduring relationships, then always be genuine.

Developing a relationship does not have to be difficult. Periodic lunches, coffee meetups, phone calls, emails, or text messages work just fine. All it takes is a little effort. Bring value to the relationship by taking a genuine interest in the other person's life. Each relationship is different and is built upon different grounds, so you will need to adjust how you build each one. For instance, a relationship that started with playing pickup racquetball could be nurtured by simply playing more racquetball. A relationship that begins through a conversation at a career fair could be developed through periodic coffee meetups or email conversations. You will need to gauge how you approach and develop each relationship based on your specific circumstances.

Step 3: Pay it Forward. The third and final step in creating a good network is to pay it forward. Once you have established yourself and landed the career you desire, don't forget where you started. Remember that there are plenty of young engineers who are struggling to find their way, just like you were. Help and teach them what you know. Knowledge is wasted unless it is shared. Not to mention, it feels good to help people!

We live in a world full of people. And your connections with those people can lift you into places that would have been unachievable on your own.

Internships

There is a common dilemma that many engineers face after graduation. They enter the job market eager and excited to begin their careers only to find that most job postings for entry-level engineers prefer one to two years of experience in that field. "Wait...what? How is that possible if I haven't even graduated yet?" You guessed it—the answer is an internship. An internship bridges that gap between being a newly graduated student with no experience and one with just enough experience to be desirable. An internship can give you that little edge you need when you make the leap from student to professional.

An internship is by far the best way to gain real-world engineering experience while you're still a student. As an intern, you will gain real insight into what an engineer actually does day-to-day. You will be exposed to technical communication, presentation, teamwork, engineering analysis, problem-solving, and design, which is exactly the experience you'll want when you're trying to decide what to do after graduation. An internship will also provide the ever-so-important résumé boost. In the upcoming section, we will explore the most important aspects of finding and landing a great internship.

Not All Are Created Equal: Internships vary significantly in length, job responsibility, pay, schedule, and benefits. Some positions last only for a summer, while others are year-round (year-round positions are more often called co-ops). Some consist mostly of boring grunt work, while others offer more complex and engaging projects. Some are part time and others are full time. Some are nonpaying, while others pay very well. Some will come with no benefits, while others will come with a full benefits package including health insurance, life insurance, 401(k), and even tuition reimbursement. As you can see, one internship can vary significantly from another. You will need to weigh these factors during your search. Some questions you should ask yourself are, "How much time can I commit? How much money do I need to make? Do I need insurance and other benefits? Is the position important enough for me to make concessions in schedule, pay, and benefits?" Keep these questions in mind, and they will guide you to a position that best suits your personal situation.

Grades: I'm not going to sugarcoat it. When it comes to landing an internship, your grades are important, plain and simple. Yes, it sucks to have the entirety of your value summed up into one little number. But without any related work experience, GPA is basically the only solid metric that companies can use to differentiate between candidates. It is just the reality of the world we live in. Based on my research and personal experience, the minimum GPA for most large companies is in the 3.0 to 3.25 range. You can compensate for a lower GPA with some solid networking, interviewing skills, and a great résumé. However, the cold hard truth remains the same—the higher the GPA, the better chance you have at getting an interview.

PRO TIP: List your highest GPA on your résumé. You may not know this, but you have two GPAs. First, your cumulative GPA, which includes every course you have ever taken. Second, your major GPA, which includes only the courses that will count toward your degree. Use whichever one is higher on your résumé.

Use Your Network: We have already covered the importance of networking in the previous section. But it's worth touching on again here. If you're plagued by a low GPA, developing a solid network should be a top priority for you. Find friends who already have internships. Ask them for advice with your résumé and interviewing skills. Ask them if they'd be willing to help you get an interview. Attend any and all events where you could potentially make some good contacts. I can't overstate the potential significance that just one relationship can hold. Take every opportunity to meet people and start conversations. Only good things can come from it.

Apply, Apply, Apply: In basketball, a good way to increase your chances of making a basket is to simply take more shots. It's just plain statistics. The same could be said for landing an internship. Increase your applications, and you will increase your chances of getting an interview.

Don't Be Picky: Apply for anything and everything. Even if you don't love the company, interview experience is extremely valuable and should be gathered up anywhere you can get it.

Go to Career Fairs: Yes, they can be a little uncomfortable and intimidating (basically speed dating for internships). But

195

real opportunities can come from them (I actually got a legitimate interview and high paying job offer directly from a career fair). Keep in mind that career fairs are held at all colleges. Research your surrounding schools and go to them all!

Applying Online: Besides the obvious job search websites like Indeed, Monster, and CareerBuilder, don't forget to check individual company websites. Many times, you will find job postings that aren't listed on the major job search sites.

Apply Outside of Your Market: The market you live in may be flooded with applicants, but other markets may be starved. Don't forget to apply to out-of-state and international employers. Why not? If you get discouraged, just remember that with enough applications, résumé iterations, and interviews, you're bound to land an internship eventually. It's just a numbers game. With enough shots, you will eventually score.

Résumé: Think of your résumé as a real person. More specifically, think of your résumé as you—a version of you that you send to represent your capabilities and interests before you arrive for any potential interview. Once you view a résumé in this way, you will realize that your first impression has already taken place well before you meet anyone in the flesh. How do you want to be judged? Do you want to look like someone who does the bare minimum and is too lazy to care about proper detail? Or do you want to look like someone who is organized, detailed, and gets the job done right? Believe it or not, many employers will unconsciously make these types of judgments based only on your résumé, so do not take its creation lightly. I have worked as an engineering manager, and I can tell you that your résumé literally holds the keys to an interview. With that, let's go over the three primary characteristics that define a professional résumé: content, structure, and presentation.

⇒ **Content:** At a minimum, every résumé should contain the following four items: related work experience, education, related skills/certifications, and contact info. You probably already knew that. But what you might not know is that the content of your résumé should change based on the job you're applying for. Because in this day and age, the first person that will see your résumé may not actually be a person but an algorithm.

More and more companies these days are using applicant tracking software (ATS) in an attempt to be more efficient in the hiring process, especially large companies that get hundreds of résumés per day. The ATS is programmed to only let the most qualified applicants through to an actual human recruiter. The programming focuses on three things: keywords, simplicity, and grammar.

⇒ **Keywords:** Tailor your résumé's content with phrases, acronyms, and keywords from the actual job description. The ATS software will like this.

⇒ **Simplicity:** ATS likes simplicity. Stick with Microsoft Word or PDF formats and a normal font like Times New Roman. Get rid of pictures, figures, or charts, and don't let it get too wordy. Your résumé should be a short summary, not a life story.

⇒ **Grammar:** ATS hates grammar errors. It would be a shame to be denied a job because you didn't know that "alot" isn't a word (I do it all the time). Proofread your résumé multiple times, use software to check its grammar and spelling, and have a friend or family member verify it's clean before you submit it to any posting.

⇒ **Structure:** The structure of your résumé should be based on what you want the reader to see first. With that in mind, any related work and professional experience should usually come first, followed by education and skills respectively. You should assume that the reader only has a few seconds to decide between your résumé and other applicants, then organize accordingly.

⇒ **Presentation and Formatting:** Good presentation and formatting can go a long way in demonstrating your attention to detail and general efficiency. Outside of what the words actually say, ask yourself if your résumé is pleasing to look at. Some things to consider here are even space utilization, formatting consistency, and overall symmetry.

- **Space Utilization:** Try to utilize the full page evenly. Play with the margins, fonts, and spacing to create an even usage of the space.

- **Formatting Consistency:** Make sure that you use the exact same formatting style from section to section. Random formatting changes can distract the reader from important content. Make sure that you're consistent with spacing, bullet usage, font sizes, and margins. Trust me, people notice these details.

- **Symmetry:** Humans love symmetry. We love to look at things that are even and balanced. Take advantage of this fact when formatting your résumé. Try to space content with symmetry in mind. It will go a long way in helping your résumé become more visually appealing.

Interviewing

If there is one thing that can even the playing field between a less qualified candidate and a more qualified one, it's a great interview. I truly believe that interviewing is one of the most underrated skills that any new engineer can cultivate. Just think about it. An average interview only lasts between thirty and ninety minutes. But in that short amount of time, you have the opportunity to convince someone that they not only want to work with you for forty hours a week for the foreseeable future but also want to pay you a lot of money for it. There are not many other times in your life where so much will depend on such a short event. Below we will explore some of the most important aspects of interview preparation and performance.

Before the Interview: The preparation for any evaluation should be proportional to its potential impact on your life. When you view an interview through this lens, it is obvious that we could all spend more time on interview preparation. Below I have listed some of the most important steps to take when preparing for an interview.

⇒ **Prepare Questions:** Spend some hours researching the company and specific role you're interviewing for. Then prepare a list of good questions to ask based on this research. Also, never ever ask about benefits or compensation during an interview. These questions can wait until after an offer is made.

⇒ **Have Answers and Examples Ready:** No two interviews are the same. However, there are a few questions that tend to always show up in one form or another. Have answers prepared for these common questions:

- What are your strengths and weaknesses?

199

- How do you deal with conflict?
- Describe a time when you overcame adversity.
- Describe a time when you failed and how you learned from it.
- Describe a time when you were successful.
- Why should we hire you over someone else with the same credentials?

⇒ **Practice, Practice, Practice:** How do you become proficient at anything? Practice! Grab a friend or family member and have them run through some common interview questions with you. Have them throw some curveballs to keep you on your toes. Talking about yourself is not always easy. But with practice, it will become more natural.

⇒ **Self-Presentation:** Whether we want to admit it or not, we all judge others based on appearances. If you show up for an interview in jeans, a T-shirt, and with bed head, then your interviewers may get the impression that you don't take this opportunity seriously. Consequently, they won't take you seriously. Always, always, always look your best for any interview. It shows that you are a serious candidate and are appreciative of the opportunity in front of you.

The preparation for any evaluation should be proportional to its potential impact on your life.

During the Interview: Outside of your technical capabilities, an interview is also where traits like verbal communication, nonverbal communication, teamwork, humility, trustworthiness, teachability, and overall personality will be assessed. Your interviewers will want to determine if you're not only technically qualified but also a good cultural fit for their team. Below we will examine some of the most important things to remember during an interview.

⇒ **Be Honest:** The urge to exaggerate or bolster content can be strong during an interview. You should avoid this temptation. Your interviewers will probably see right through it. You may think you're making yourself look more competent and qualified. In reality, it makes you look untrustworthy and insecure. Always be honest and straightforward in an interview.

⇒ **Take Your Time:** Have you ever found yourself rambling during an interview? Don't worry, we all do it. For some reason we feel like we need to answer questions immediately and continue talking until we are blue in the face. Try to control this impulse and remember that it is totally okay to pause and collect your thoughts before you answer any question. It shows that you're being thoughtful and genuine, and your answers will be much more clear and easier to follow. Thoughtful silence is okay!

⇒ **Be Genuinely Confident:** I know this is easier said than done. But having and showing confidence is a huge advantage during an interview. Confidence shows that you're a secure and solid investment for any employer. And if you think you have no reason to be confident, think again. The fact that a company is willing to pay their expensive management to interview you in the first place should give you confidence. Your résumé has already demonstrated that you have what they're looking for, so you have every reason to be genuinely confident. Remind

201

yourself that they want you just as much as you want them.

⇒ **Be Humble:** While confidence is a very valuable asset, too much confidence can have the opposite effect. It can make you look like an insecure braggart. Showing humility is just as important as showing confidence. Humility shows that you're teachable, self-secure, and trustworthy. Nobody is perfect. Everyone has weaknesses and makes mistakes. Don't try to hide these things. Instead, you should highlight what you learned and how you grew from your mistakes and failures. This will do so much more for you than pretending to be perfect.

Quick Recap

Due to the nature of engineering school, it may feel like there is no end. But let me be clear, graduation *will* come, school *will* end, and you *will* begin your career. With homework, labs, projects, exams, and deadlines monopolizing your attention day in and day out, it can be easy to forget this fact. Don't let yourself become ill prepared after graduation. Your first job is very important and will set the tone for the rest of your career. Don't let a nice salary blind you, and be patient. The perfect career is out there; you just need to find it.

To avoid being unprepared, you should begin planning for your life after school as early as possible. The first step is to narrow down what you actually want to do with your degree. Assess your career aspirations frequently. If you aren't totally sure about what your interests are, get out of your comfort zone and try new things. Do research on different career options and talk to other engineers in those careers. Then once you do have a good idea of your desired career path, begin pursuing that path aggressively. A good place to start is building your network. Develop real relationships with as many other students, professors, and engineers as you can. Help people, and people will help you. Next, make landing an internship a high priority. It is crucial in bridging the gap between an inexperienced graduate and one with just enough experience to be desirable. Build your résumé and apply to every position possible, even if it's not your dream job—the interview experience is extremely valuable. By taking these actions early, you will be securing yourself a much more seamless transition from student to working engineer.

Final Thoughts

Society has long held the belief that the prerequisite for an engineering degree is a massive IQ and a pocket protector. I'm here to tell you that this just isn't true. Anyone can do it, and I am the proof. Your brain can adapt and grow through self-discipline, persistence, and motivation. These traits are the true requirements for an engineering degree. I barely squeaked by in high school and scored a seventeen on the ACT. Yet I graduated with two engineering degrees with a 3.8 GPA. If I can do it, so can you. Students don't drop out because they aren't smart enough. They drop out because they weren't prepared for the workload and adversity. The truth is that you're capable of this. But being capable of something and actually accomplishing it are quite different.

⇒ To start, the strength of your motivation must be proportional to the effort required to graduate. How much do you want it? What are you willing to endure?

⇒ Next, you must develop the self-discipline required to strengthen and grow your mental capacity and capabilities. By establishing and cultivating new study habits, your mind will slowly form new neural pathways, making

203

it easier and more fluid to understand and retain complex material.

⇒ It's important to remember that progress does not happen overnight. On average, you should expect engineering school to demand twenty to fifty hours per week depending on your course load. Do you currently have this much free time available? Take steps before school begins to free up an appropriate amount of space in your schedule because you're going to need it.

⇒ By injecting sustainability and efficiency into your schedule, lifestyle, and mind-set, you will be setting yourself up for prolonged success.

⇒ Next, you'll need to learn how to learn. Becoming an effective studier is vital. Keep developing your study process until it is effective and you're seeing success.

⇒ Finally, all of this comes together to produce results—exam results. Because more than anything else, exams are the metric that your grades are weighted upon. You must approach and prepare for them with proportional effort and seriousness.

Engineering school will be challenging and at times even heartbreaking. But it will also be fun, exhilarating, and most importantly, extremely fulfilling. It is the type of audacious challenge that can really transform a person for the better—the type of challenge that you really should be seeking out in life. It was the best decision I ever made, and I sincerely hope that my experience and the material in this book have shown you that you can do the same. You can do this!

Acknowledgements

Thank you to the students, professors, and professionals who provided the insight I needed. Thank you to my undergraduate study group for helping me grow. Thank you to my incredible wife for showing me how to be a good partner. Thank you to my amazing daughter for opening my eyes to the world all over again. And thank you to my parents for giving me the tools to build anything.

Connect with me:

YouTube channel: Becoming an Engineer
Email: becominganengineer123@gmail.com

If you found this book helpful, please leave a review on Amazon!

Printed in Great Britain
by Amazon

35982920R00117